STECK-VAUGHN   LEVEL F

MAPS · GLOBES · GRAPHS

AN INTERACTIVE PROGRAM

Writer

Henry Billings

Consultants

Marian Gregory
Teacher
San Luis Coastal Unified
    School District
San Luis Obispo, California

Norman McRae, Ph.D.
Former Director of Fine
    Arts and Social Studies
Detroit Public Schools
Detroit, Michigan

Marilyn Nebenzahl
Social Studies Consultant
San Francisco, California

Gloria Sesso
Supervisor of Social Studies
Half Hollow Hills School
    District
Dix Hills, New York

Edna Whitfield
Former Social Studies
    Supervisor
St. Louis Public Schools
St. Louis, Missouri

Karen Wiggins
Director of Social Studies
Richardson Independent
    School District
Richardson, Texas

STECK-VAUGHN
C O M P A N Y
A Subsidiary of National Education Corporation

Acknowledgments

Staff Credits Executive Editor: Diane Sharpe
Project Editor: Anne Souby
Art Director: D. Childress
Designer: Richard Balsam

Cover Design Linda Adkins Graphic Design

**Cover
Photography** Cooke Photographics

Illustration Michael Krone–4, 5, 6, 7, 8, 9, 34 inset, 59, 64
David Griffin–40, 65 inset, 66 inset

Graphics Richard Balsam

Cartography Land Registration and Information Service
    Amherst, Nova Scotia, Canada
Gary J. Robinson
Maryland Cartographics Incorporated
R. R. Donnelley and Sons Company

ISBN 0-8114-6205-6

Contents

1 • Globes

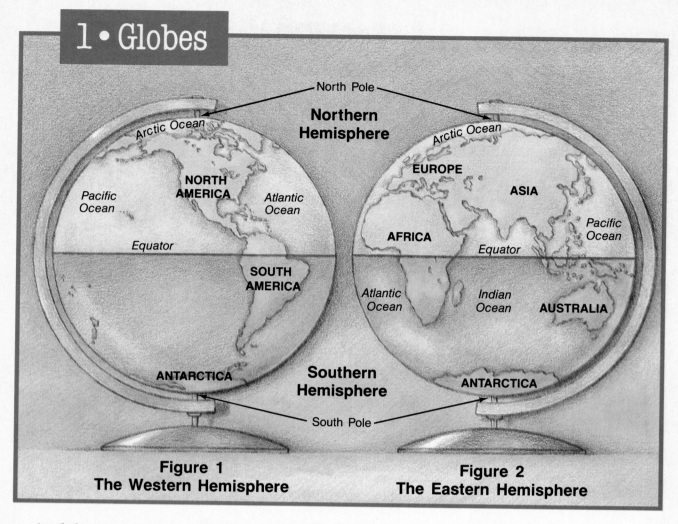

Figure 1
The Western Hemisphere

Figure 2
The Eastern Hemisphere

A **globe** is a model of Earth, which is shaped somewhat like a sphere, or ball. Globes show **continents** and **oceans**, the large land and water masses on Earth. Find the seven continents and four oceans on Figures 1 and 2 above.

Some points and imaginary lines help us find places on Earth. The **North Pole** and the **South Pole** are the places farthest north and south on Earth. We use the poles to know the four main directions, north, south, east, and west.

Find the **Equator** on Figures 1 and 2. This imaginary circle around the middle of Earth divides Earth into two hemispheres. **Hemisphere** means half a sphere or globe. The hemisphere north of the Equator is called the Northern Hemisphere. The hemisphere south of the Equator is called the Southern Hemisphere.

The globe can also be divided into the Eastern Hemisphere and the Western Hemisphere. Figure 1 shows the Western Hemisphere. Figure 2 shows the Eastern Hemisphere.

► If you stand on the North Pole, what is the only direction you can go?
  If you stand on the South Pole, what is the only direction you can go?

► Name the seven continents and the four oceans.
  Which continents and oceans are in the Eastern Hemisphere?
  Which are in the Western Hemisphere?

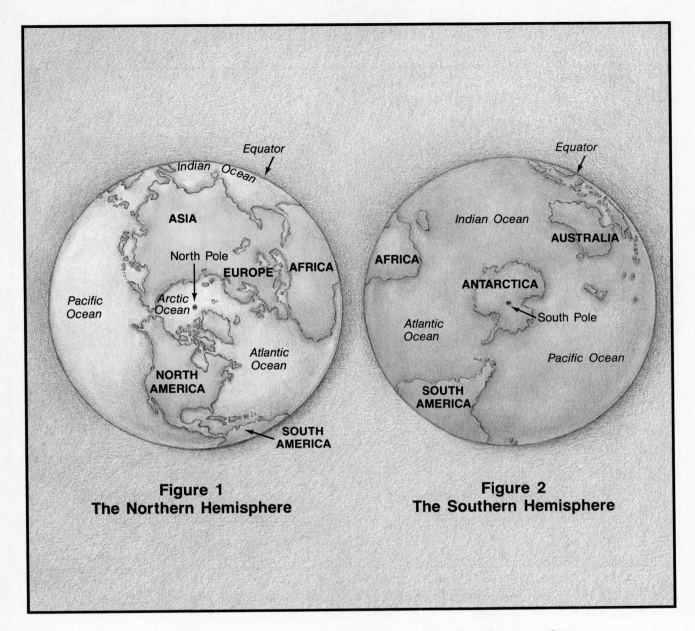

Figure 1
The Northern Hemisphere

Figure 2
The Southern Hemisphere

Figures 1 and 2 show a different way of looking at the Northern and Southern Hemispheres. Figure 1 shows the Northern Hemisphere with the North Pole in the center. What continents do you recognize? Look back at the hemispheres on page 4 to help you identify the continents.

Figure 2 shows the Southern Hemisphere with the South Pole in the center. The South Pole is on which continent? What other continents do you see?

► Can you find the Equator on both Figure 1 and Figure 2?

► Which oceans are in the Southern Hemisphere? Which are in the Northern? Which continents are entirely in the Southern Hemisphere? Which continents are entirely in the Northern Hemisphere? Which have parts in both the Northern and Southern Hemispheres?

► Most of the land is in which hemisphere? Most of the water is in which hemisphere?

Mastering the Eastern and Western Hemispheres

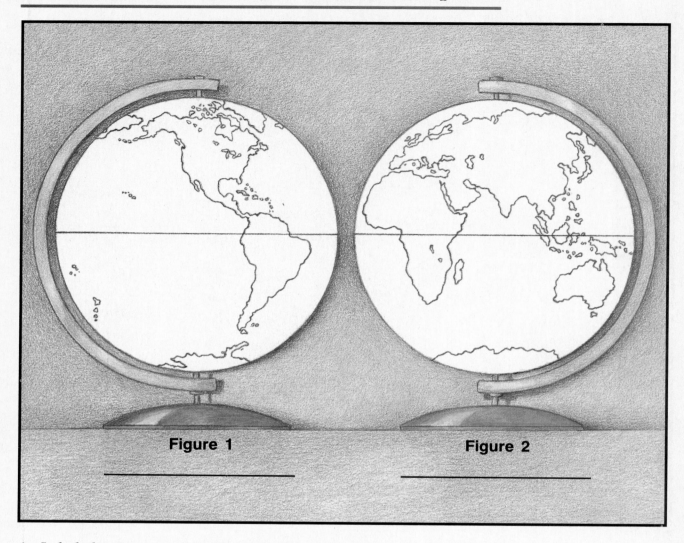

Figure 1 _____

Figure 2 _____

1. Label the Eastern and Western Hemispheres on the lines under Figures 1 and 2. Look back at page 4 if you need help.
2. Label the North Pole, South Pole, and Equator on each globe.
3. Label the continents and oceans on Figures 1 and 2. Again, look back at page 4 if you need help.
4. Which two continents are entirely in the Western Hemisphere?

   _____

5. Which four continents are entirely or mostly in the Eastern

   Hemisphere? _____

   _____

6. Which continent is almost evenly divided between the Eastern and

   Western Hemispheres? _____

7. Which ocean is entirely in the Eastern Hemisphere? _____

Mastering the Northern and Southern Hemispheres

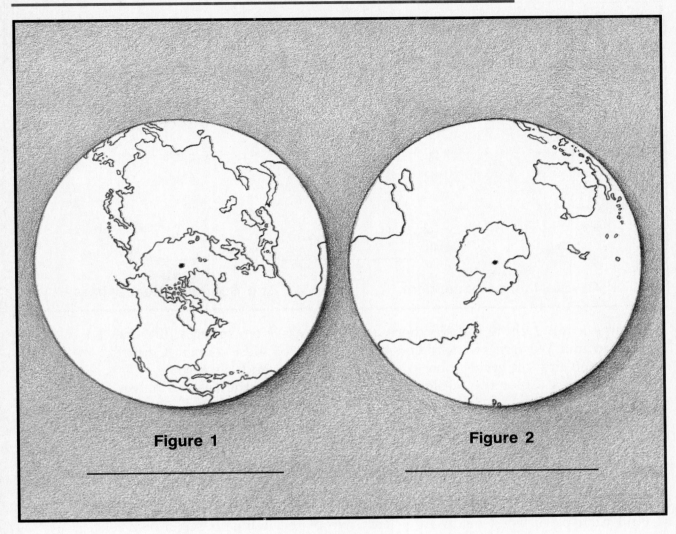

Figure 1

Figure 2

_____   _____

1. Label the North Pole, the South Pole, and the Equator on each globe. Look back at page 5 if you need help.
2. Label the Northern and Southern Hemispheres on the lines under Figures 1 and 2.
3. Label the continents and oceans on each hemisphere.
4. From the South Pole, the only direction you can go is _____.
5. From the North Pole, the only direction you can go is _____.
6. Which two continents are only in the Southern Hemisphere?

   _____

7. Which three continents are only in the Northern Hemisphere?

   _____

8. Draw an arrow pointing from South America to Africa on Figure 2.

   Which direction is that arrow pointing? _____

Mastering the Four Hemispheres

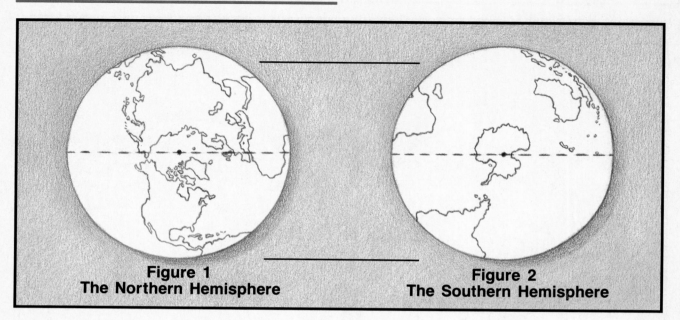

Figure 1
The Northern Hemisphere

Figure 2
The Southern Hemisphere

1. Figures 1 and 2 show the Northern and Southern Hemispheres. But the Eastern and Western Hemispheres are also part of these globes. Connect the dotted line on each globe to show the Eastern and Western Hemispheres. Color the western halves yellow. Color the eastern halves orange.

2. Label the Western Hemisphere and Eastern Hemisphere on the lines where they belong.

3. What point is at the center of the Northern Hemisphere? _____

4. What point is at the center of the Southern Hemisphere? _____

5. Find each place listed below in at least two of the hemispheres shown above. Some continents and oceans are in three or four hemispheres. Name the hemispheres in which you find each place.

    a. North America: _____

    b. Pacific Ocean: _____

    c. Arctic Ocean: _____

    d. Europe: _____

    e. Atlantic Ocean: _____

    f. Australia: _____

    g. Indian Ocean: _____

    h. Africa: _____

    i. Asia: _____

Skill Check

Vocabulary Check   **North Pole   South Pole   globe**
                        Equator   hemispheres   oceans
                        continents

Write the word or phrase that makes each sentence true.

1. The _____ is the place farthest north on Earth.

2. The Equator divides Earth into two _____.

3. A _____ is a model that shows the shape of Earth.

4. Earth's _____ and _____ are large land and water masses.

Globe Check

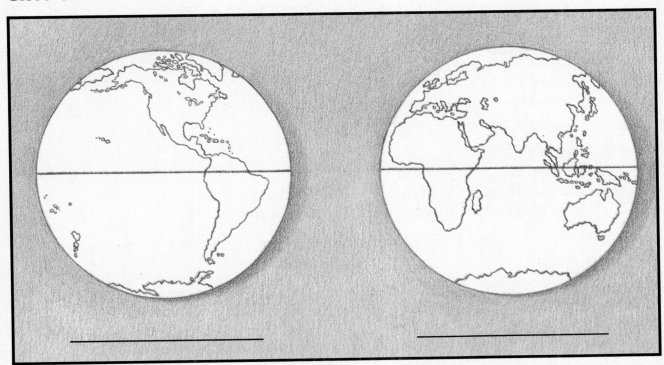

1. Label the hemispheres you see. Then label the continents, the oceans, the poles, and the Equator on each globe.

2. Which three continents are closest to the North Pole? _____

   _____

3. Besides Antarctica, which three continents are closest to the South Pole?

   _____

4. What point on Earth is farthest from the North Pole?

   _____

2 • Symbols and Directions

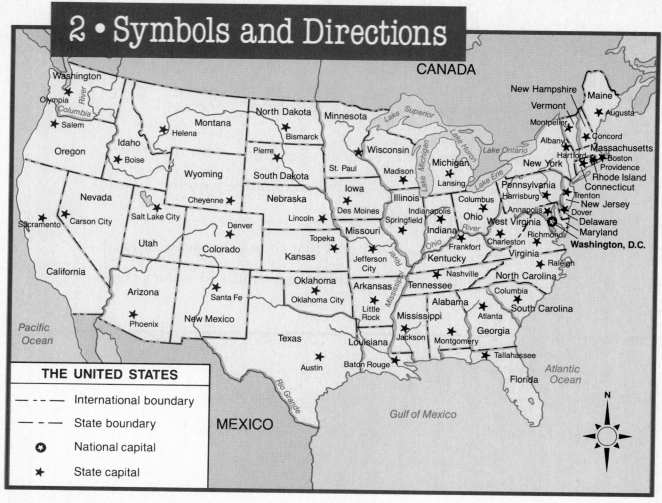

THE UNITED STATES

— – —	International boundary
– – –	State boundary
✪	National capital
★	State capital

A **map** is a flat drawing of any place. To understand a map, you must read it. Follow these steps to read and understand a map.

☑ Map Attack!

- **Read the title.** Just as a book's title tells you what you are reading, a map's title tells you what the map shows. What does this map's title tell you?
- **Read the map legend.** The legend, or key, explains the symbols on the map. What symbols are in the map legend? Find examples of each symbol on the map.
- **Read the compass rose.** The compass rose always shows north. The north arrow points to the North Pole. Once you find north you can find the other **cardinal directions**, east (E), west (W), and south (S). The compass rose often shows the **intermediate directions**: northwest (NW), southwest (SW), northeast (NE), and southeast (SE). Find the compass rose on the map. Then find each direction.

► From the capital city of Kentucky, in what direction is the capital of each of these states: Indiana, South Carolina, Ohio, Virginia, Tennessee, and Florida?

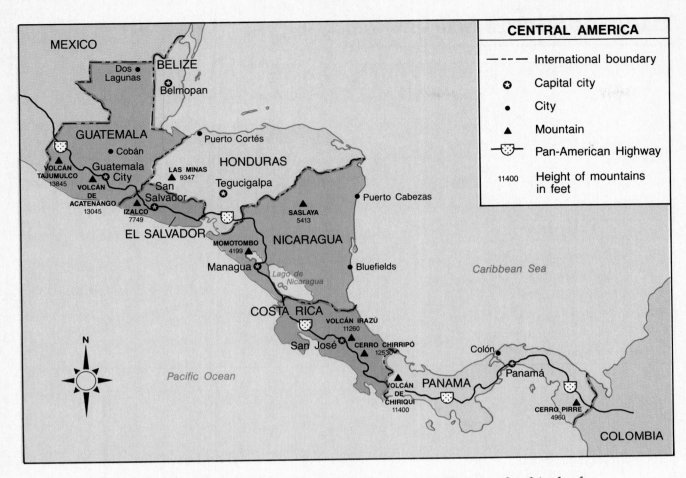

Not all maps show the same information. The title tells you the kind of information you can learn from the map. The legend explains the special symbols used on the map. Follow the **Map Attack!** steps to understand the information on this map.

☑️ **Map Attack!**

✔ **Read the title.** What part of the world is shown on this map?

✔ **Read the legend.** What major highway is shown on this map? What kind of landform is shown?

✔ **Read the compass rose.** Where is the North Pole from Central America?

Notice on the map above that the labels are not all the same size. Labels for the largest places on a map are usually large and sometimes are shown in all capital letters. Labels for water are often blue.

▶ What countries make up Central America?

▶ The Pan American Highway crosses which countries?

▶ Which country has the highest mountains? How high are they? How do you know?

▶ Which mountain is farthest east?

Mastering Symbols and Directions

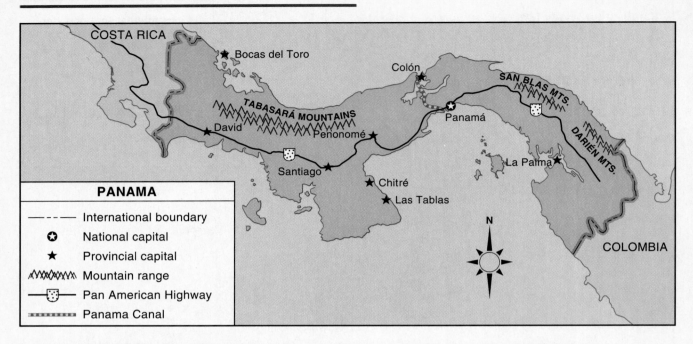

Map Attack!

✔ **Read the title.** This map shows _____.
✔ **Read the legend.** What symbols are in the legend? Find an example of each symbol on the map.
✔ **Read the compass rose.** Find north. Then label the remaining points.

1. Label these bodies of water. Look back at page 11 for help.

   Caribbean Sea   Pacific Ocean

2. What country borders Panama on the east? _____

3. What country borders Panama on the west? _____

4. How many mountain ranges are shown on the map? _____

5. Find these pairs of places on the map. What direction would you travel to get from the first place to the second place? Write the abbreviation of the correct cardinal or intermediate direction.

   a. Bocas del Toro to David   _____

   b. Santiago to Penonomé   _____

   c. the national capital to La Palma   _____

   d. Colón to Chitré   _____

   e. Las Tablas to Santiago   _____

6. Is the Pan American Highway north or south of the mountain ranges? _____

Mastering Symbols and Directions

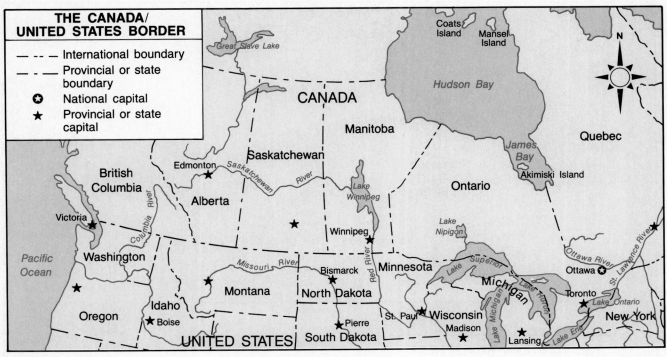

THE CANADA/ UNITED STATES BORDER

- – - — International boundary
- – · — Provincial or state boundary
- ⊗ National capital
- ★ Provincial or state capital

☑️ Map Attack!

Follow the steps on page 12 to begin reading this map.

1. Trace the boundary between Canada and the United States in red.
2. Trace the state and province boundaries in green.
3. Label these capital cities.

   Salem, Oregon   Regina, Saskatchewan
   Quebec, Quebec   Helena, Montana

4. Victoria, British Columbia, is on Vancouver Island. Label Vancouver Island.
5. What state and province does the Columbia River flow through?

   _____

6. What large lake is in central Manitoba? _____
7. Lake Superior forms a boundary for what states and province?

   _____

8. What island is in James Bay? _____
9. What direction would you travel to get from Lansing to Toronto? _____

   From Manitoba to Alberta? _____
10. The Red River forms a boundary between what two states?

   _____

Mastering Directions on a Map

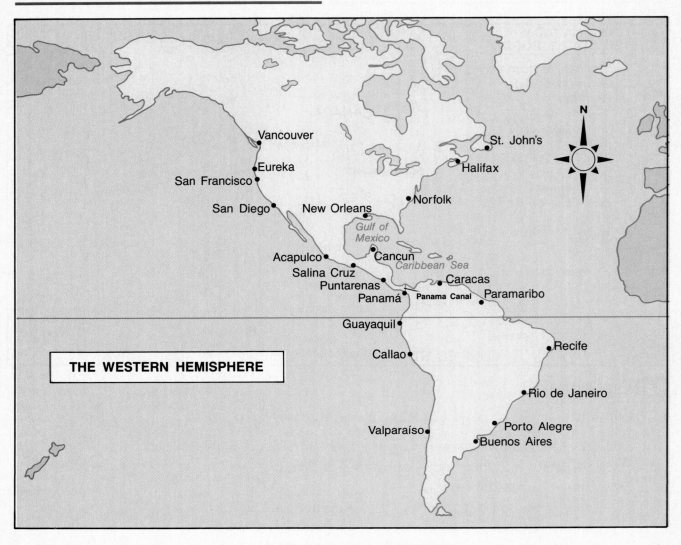

1. Write the following labels where they belong on this map.
   NORTH AMERICA   SOUTH AMERICA   PACIFIC OCEAN
   ATLANTIC OCEAN   Equator

2. Plan an ocean cruise along the western coast of North America.
   Begin in Vancouver. Name, in order, four other port cities on your
   route.

   _____

3. Sail from the western coast to the eastern coast through the

   Panama Canal. What body of water do you enter? _____

4. Continue sailing south along the eastern coast of South America.
   Name, in order, four port cities along this route.

   _____

5. Trace your route from Vancouver to Buenos Aires in red. Circle the
   cities on the route.

Skill Check

Vocabulary Check

map	**title** **compass rose**
intermediate directions	**legend** **cardinal directions**

Write the word or phrase that best completes each sentence.

1. A _____ is a flat drawing of a place.

2. North, south, east, and west are _____.

3. You can find north on a map by looking at the _____.

4. The map's _____ explains the map's symbols.

5. The map's _____ tells you what the map shows.

Map Check

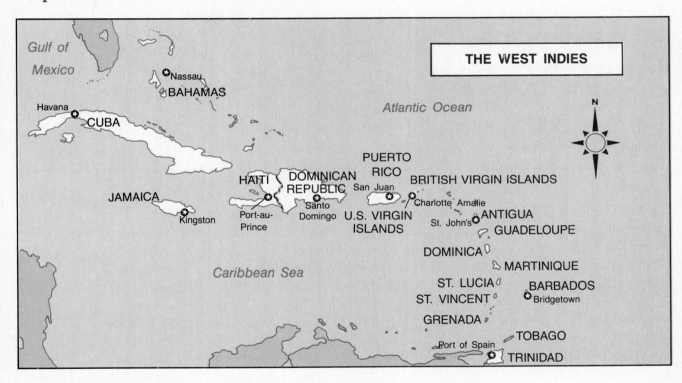

1. Highlight each of these countries using a separate, light color.

   Cuba   Jamaica   Haiti   Dominican Republic

2. On the map, draw an arrow from the first place to the second place in each pair. In which direction does each arrow point? Write the correct abbreviation for each direction below.

   Nassau to Havana _____   Dominican Republic to Haiti _____

   Bridgetown to St. Vincent _____   Jamaica to Antigua _____

   San Juan to Charlotte Amalie _____   Trinidad to Tobago _____

3 • Scale and Distance

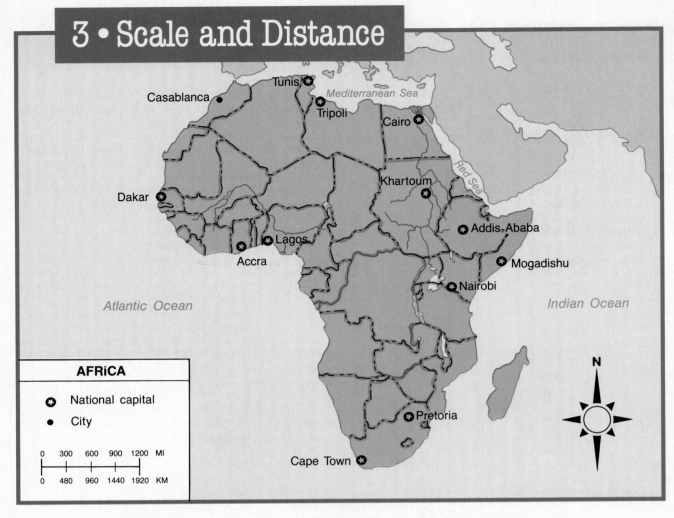

Maps can show the actual shape of a place. They cannot show the actual size of a place. The size of the place must be reduced to fit on a piece of paper. To help us figure distances, maps are drawn to scale. **Scale** is used to keep the shape of a place <u>and</u> show the distances. On the map of Africa above, the scale is "1 inch = 1,200 miles or 1,920 kilometers." A **map scale** shows the relationship of the actual distance on Earth to the distance on a map.

Map scales often show distance in miles (MI) and kilometers (KM). Find the map scale on the map above.

Miles and **kilometers** are two units of length used to measure distance. In the United States, distances are usually measured in miles. In many other countries the usual measurement is kilometers.

Find Dakar and Accra on the map of Africa above. They are only one inch apart. But how far apart are they on Earth? To find out, use the map scale and a ruler, a string, or the edge of a paper to figure the number of miles or kilometers between Dakar and Accra. The distance is about 1,200 miles or 1,920 kilometers.

► What is the distance between Khartoum and Addis Ababa?
  Find the distance in miles and kilometers.

► What is the distance between Tripoli and Cape Town?
  Find the distance in miles and in kilometers.

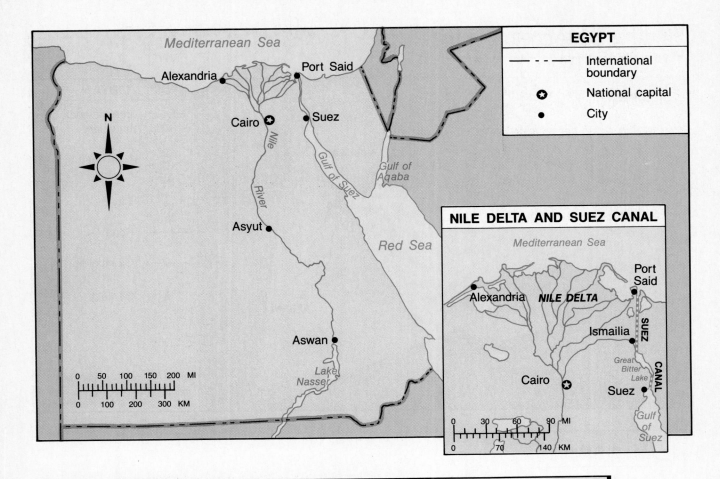

Map Attack! Add a step to read the maps.

- ✔ **Read the title.** What can you learn from these maps?
- ✔ **Read the legend.** Find each symbol on the maps.
- ✔ **Read the compass rose.** Find north on each map.
- ✔ **Read the map scales.** How does the scale differ on each map?

The scale is not the same on all maps. Look at the two maps above. The larger map shows all of Egypt. The smaller map is an inset map that shows only part of Egypt: the Nile Delta and the Suez Canal. An **inset map** is a small map within a larger map. An inset map may have its own scale.

► Compare the scales on the two maps.

► Measure the distance between Suez and Port Said on the map of Egypt. What is the distance?

► Measure the distance between Suez and Port Said on the inset map. What is the distance?

► On which map is it easier to measure distances?

► Can you measure the distance between Ismailia and Asyut? Why or why not?

► How could you figure the distance between Ismailia and Asyut using both of the maps?

Finding Distances in Libya

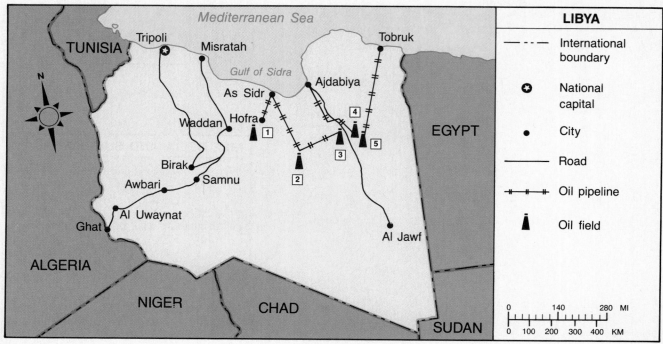

LIBYA	
- - -	International boundary
✪	National capital
•	City
———	Road
+++	Oil pipeline
▲	Oil field

Scale:
0 140 280 MI
0 100 200 300 400 KM

☑ Map Attack!

✔ **Read the title.** This map shows _____.

✔ **Read the legend.** Check (✔) each symbol in the legend and a matching symbol on the map.

✔ **Read the compass rose.** Complete the compass rose.

✔ **Read the map scale.** The length of the scale stands for how many miles? _____ how many kilometers? _____

1. Trace each oil pipeline. Then find its length.

   a. Hofra to As Sidr   _____ KM   _____ MI

   b. Oil field #2 to As Sidr   _____ KM   _____ MI

   c. Oil field #4 to Ajdabiya _____ KM   _____ MI

   d. Oil field #5 to Tobruk   _____ KM   _____ MI

2. a. Which oil pipeline covers the longest distance?

   _____

   b. Which oil pipeline covers the shortest distance?

   _____

3. Draw a conclusion. Where do all the oil pipelines in Libya go?

   _____ Why? _____

Finding Distances in Southern Africa

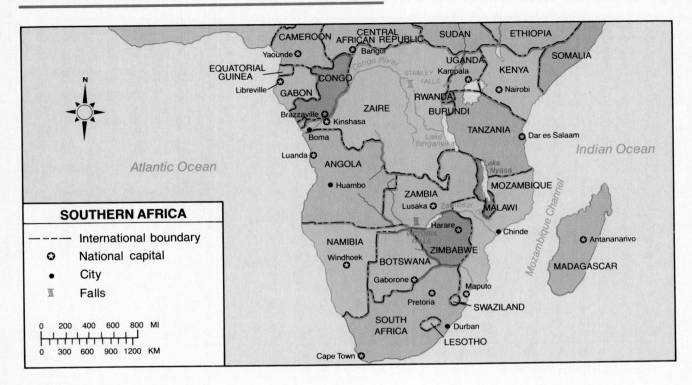

SOUTHERN AFRICA

- – – – International boundary
- ✪ National capital
- • City
- ⊠ Falls

```
0   200  400  600  800  MI
|---|---|---|---|---|---|---|
0   300  600  900  1200  KM
```

☑ Map Attack!

Follow the steps on page 18 to begin reading this map.

1. Draw a line from the first place to the second. Then find the distance.

    a. Cape Town to Windhoek   _____ KM   _____ MI

    b. Windhoek to Kinshasa   _____ KM   _____ MI

    c. Kinshasa to Bangui   _____ KM   _____ MI

    d. Bangui to Kampala   _____ KM   _____ MI

    e. Kampala to Nairobi   _____ KM   _____ MI

    f. Nairobi to Maputo   _____ KM   _____ MI

    g. Maputo to Cape Town   _____ KM   _____ MI

2. What is the total distance of this trip? _____ KM   _____ MI

3. Trace the Congo River from Stanley Falls to Boma.

    Use the map scale to estimate this distance. _____ KM   _____ MI

4. Trace the Zambezi River from Victoria Falls to Chinde.

    Use the map scale to estimate this distance. _____ KM   _____ MI

5. Which river trip is longer? _____

Finding Distances in Northern Africa

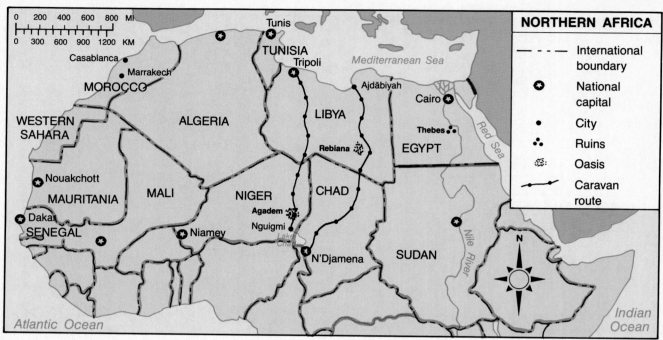

1. The Mediterranean Sea is a boundary for what countries? _____

   _____

2. Label these capital cities.
   a. Algiers, Algeria
   b. Khartoum, Sudan
   c. Bamako, Mali

3. Trace the caravan route from Tripoli, Libya to Nguigmi, Niger.

   a. What direction does it go? _____

   b. What oasis does it pass by? _____

   c. From Tripoli to Nguigmi is about _____ km. or _____ mi.

4. Find the distance between the following cities and the direction from the
   first city to the second.

	Distance		Direction
a. Casablanca to Marrakech	_____ KM	_____ MI	_____
b. Nouakchott to Tunis	_____ KM	_____ MI	_____
c. Dakar to Cairo	_____ KM	_____ MI	_____

5. How far are the ruins at Thebes from Cairo? _____ KM _____ MI

6. If a camel went 40 kilometers a day, how long would a trip by

   camel from Cairo to the ruins take? _____

Skill Check

Vocabulary Check   **map scale**   **inset map**   **miles (MI)**   **kilometers (KM)**

1. To show the relationship between the actual size of a place and its

   reduced size on a map, map makers use _____ .

2. Distances in the United States are usually measured in _____ .

3. Distances in countries other than the United States are usually

   measured in _____ .

Map Check

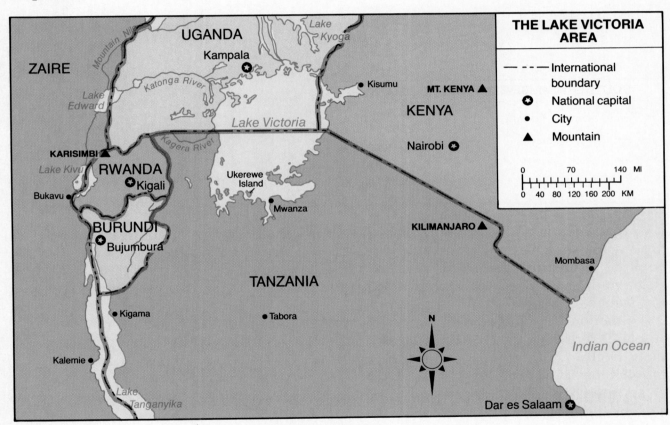

1. About how long is the border between Kenya and Tanzania?

   _____ KM   _____ MI

2. Find the distance between these places.

   a. Nairobi to Mombasa   _____ KM   _____ MI

   b. Dar es Salaam to Kigali   _____ KM   _____ MI

   c. Kampala to Bujumbura   _____ KM   _____ MI

   d. Mt. Kenya to Kilimanjaro   _____ KM   _____ MI

4 • Route Maps

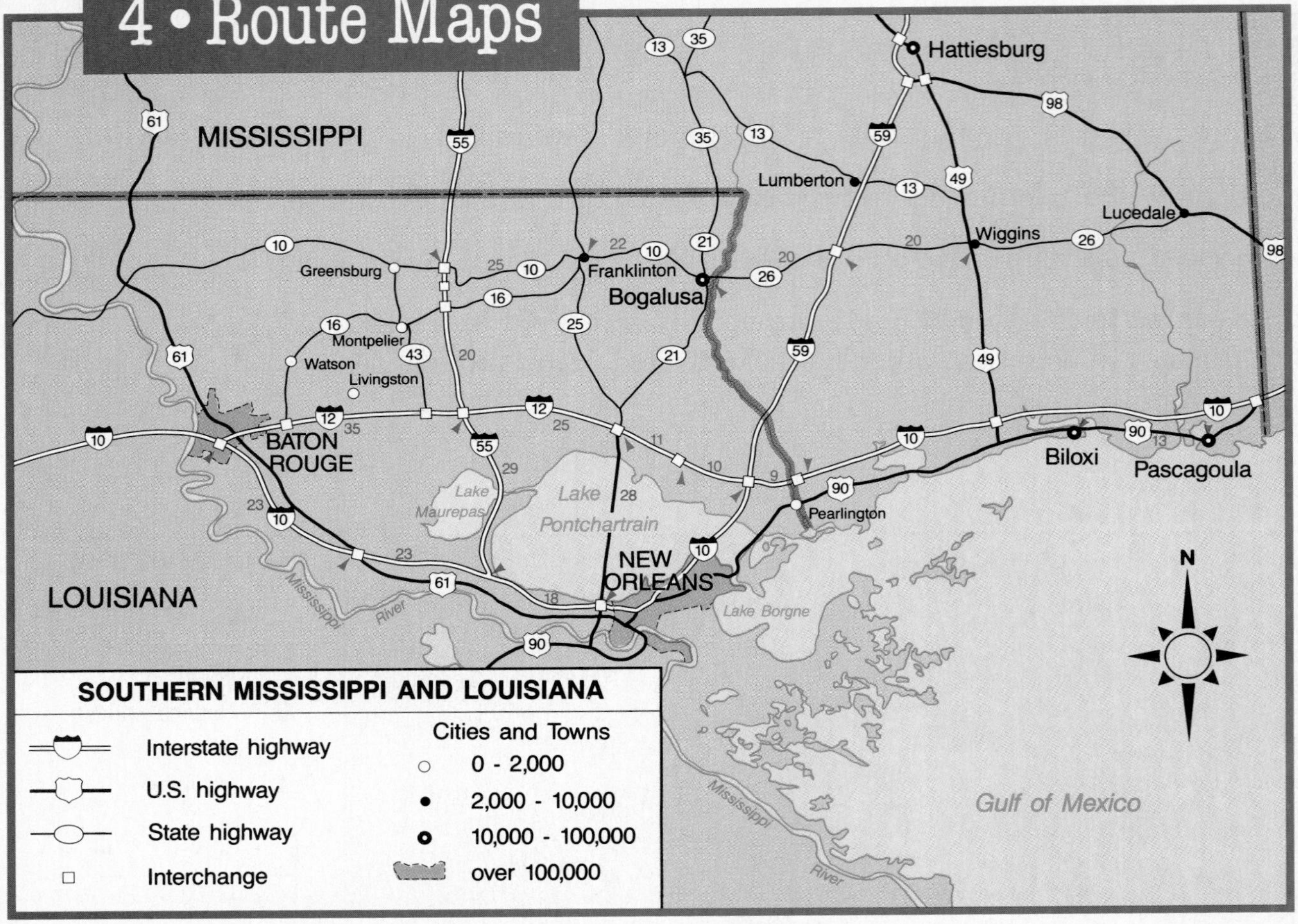
MISSISSIPPI
LOUISIANA
Hattiesburg
Lumberton
Lucedale
Wiggins
Greensburg
Franklinton
Bogalusa
Montpelier
Watson
Livingston
BATON ROUGE
NEW ORLEANS
Pearlington
Biloxi
Pascagoula
Lake Maurepas
Lake Pontchartrain
Lake Borgne
Mississippi River
Gulf of Mexico
N
SOUTHERN MISSISSIPPI AND LOUISIANA
Interstate highway
U.S. highway
State highway
Interchange
Cities and Towns
0 - 2,000
2,000 - 10,000
10,000 - 100,000
over 100,000

A road map is a kind of route map that shows the highways of an area. Road maps show several kinds of highways. Most major roads have numbers to identify them. This road map also has special symbols for cities of different sizes. Read the legend to learn the meaning of the highway and city symbols.

A **junction** is a place where two highways cross or meet. Put your finger on State Highway 26 at the right of the map. Slide your finger to the left along Highway 26. What is the first highway you cross? Where Highways 26 and 49 cross is a junction.

An **interchange** is a special kind of junction. An interchange is a place on a major highway where cars can get on or off the highway. Interchanges have special connecting ramps to allow vehicles to change roads without interrupting the flow of traffic. Find an interchange on Interstate 12.

Find the red numbers on the map between junctions and cities. These **mileage markers** give the distance in miles between each set of red triangles. What is the distance between Biloxi and Pascagoula on U.S. 90?

- ► Which city is larger, Biloxi or Pearlington?
- ► What body of water do Interstate 10 and Interstate 12 go around?
- ► Where is the junction of Highway 25 and Highway 10?
- ► If you got off Interstate 59 south of Lumberton, what highway would you be on? What is the first city you would come to going west?

Index

A street map is also a route map.

Maps often have grids. A **grid** is a pattern of lines which cross to form squares on the map. With a grid, it is easy to find places on the map. Each square in the grid is labeled with a **coordinate**. The rows of squares are labeled with a letter. The columns are labeled with a number. Each individual square has coordinates of a letter and a number. The **map index** lists places alphabetically with their grid coordinates. If you know the name of a place, and you want to find it on the map, begin by looking in the index. Find the Pharmacy Museum in the index. What are the coordinates for the Pharmacy Museum? Now find the row labeled F on the map. Slide your finger across the row until you come to column 4. Find the Pharmacy Museum in that square.

► Find Louis Armstrong Park on the map.
What two buildings are located in this park?
What street borders the park on the east?

► Find the Cabrini Doll Museum on the map.
What other building is in that column?

► Use the map index and grid to find these places on the map.
    Cafe du Monde   Preservation Hall   Orpheum Theater

► What places could you visit if you walked west on Decatur from the U.S. Mint?

Reading a Route Map

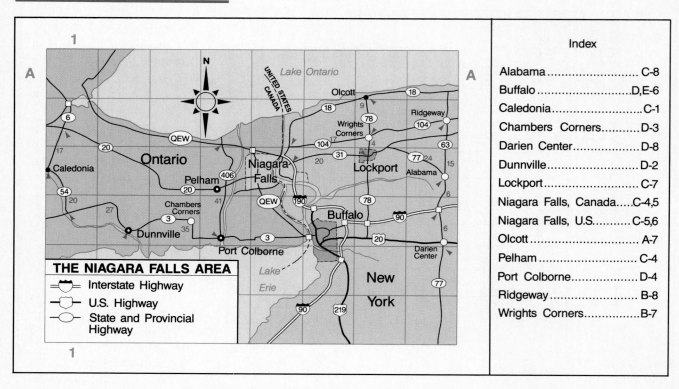

Index

THE NIAGARA FALLS AREA
- Interstate Highway
- U.S. Highway
- State and Provincial Highway

☑ Map Attack!

- ✔ **Read the title.** This map shows _____ .
- ✔ **Read the compass rose.** Label the intermediate direction arrows.
- ✔ **Read the grid and index.** Finish labeling the grid rows and columns.

1. Put an X on Niagara Falls, U.S.A. Put an O on Niagara Falls, Canada.

2. What highway enters Niagara Falls, U.S.A., from the north? _____

3. If you left Highway 20 at the first junction out of Niagara Falls and drove

   south, what city would you come to? _____

4. a. What highway goes along the north coast of Lake Erie? _____

   b. In what city could you turn north to Lake Ontario? _____

5. Circle the interchange on Interstate 90 just south of Alabama. If you
   exited I-90 at that interchange and drove north 21 miles, what city would

   you come to? _____

6. What highways form a junction at Ridgeway? _____

7. Where would you see this sign?

Niagara Falls	20
Wrights Corners	4
Alabama	24

Reading a Route Map

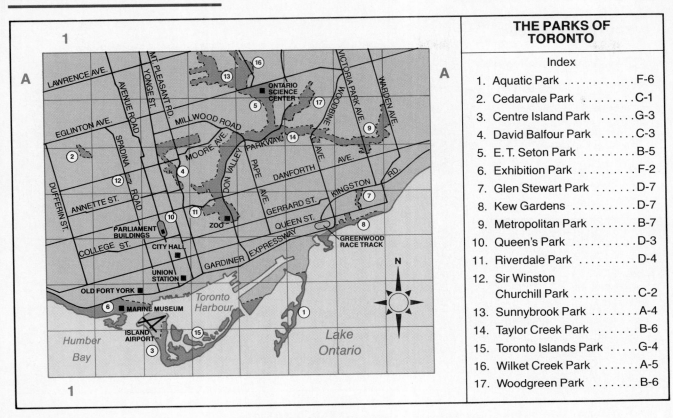

THE PARKS OF TORONTO

Index

1. Aquatic Park F-6
2. Cedarvale Park C-1
3. Centre Island Park G-3
4. David Balfour Park C-3
5. E. T. Seton Park B-5
6. Exhibition Park F-2
7. Glen Stewart Park D-7
8. Kew Gardens D-7
9. Metropolitan Park B-7
10. Queen's Park D-3
11. Riverdale Park D-4
12. Sir Winston
    Churchill Park C-2
13. Sunnybrook Park A-4
14. Taylor Creek Park B-6
15. Toronto Islands Park G-4
16. Wilket Creek Park A-5
17. Woodgreen Park B-6

1. Complete the grid by adding the missing letters and numbers.
2. Name each park described.

   a. just south of Wilket Creek Park _____

   b. in the same grid square as Woodgreen Park _____

   c. with the parliament buildings _____

   d. at the corner of Moore Ave. and Spadina Rd.

   _____

   e. on the southern end of Woodbine Ave. _____

3. What two parks are on the same island as the Island Airport?

   _____

4. What parks border the Don Valley Parkway? _____

   _____

5. What street is east of Metropolitan Park?

   _____

6. What streets would take you from Woodgreen Park to Sir Winston

   Churchill Park? _____

Reading a Route Map

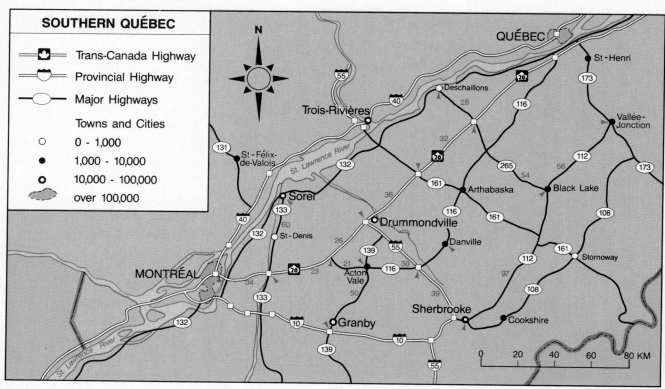

1. What highway takes you from Granby to Acton Vale? _____

2. a. How many kilometers is it from Acton Vale to the interchange just

   south of Granby? (Read the mileage marker.) _____

   b. Use the map scale to measure the distance "as the crow flies"
   (in a straight line) from Acton Vale to the interchange just south of

   Granby. The distance is _____ kilometers.

   c. Why do you think the distances differ? _____

3. a. What is the distance "as the crow flies" from Acton Vale to the

   interchange on Highway 55 southeast of Drummondville? _____

   b. What is the distance along the highway? _____

4. a. Where is the junction of Highways 112 and 265? _____

   b. If you drove 54 kilometers northwest of that junction, what junction

   would you come to? _____

5. a. What highway goes along the southern side of the St. Lawrence River?

   _____

   b. Where would you exit that highway to get to Black Lake?

   _____

Skill Check

Vocabulary Check   junction   interchange   grid
                        coordinate   mileage marker   index

Write the word or phrase that best completes each sentence.

1. A _____ is the place where two roads meet or cross.

2. An _____ is a junction of major highways and has special connecting ramps or roads.

3. A _____ indicates distance between cities.

Map Check

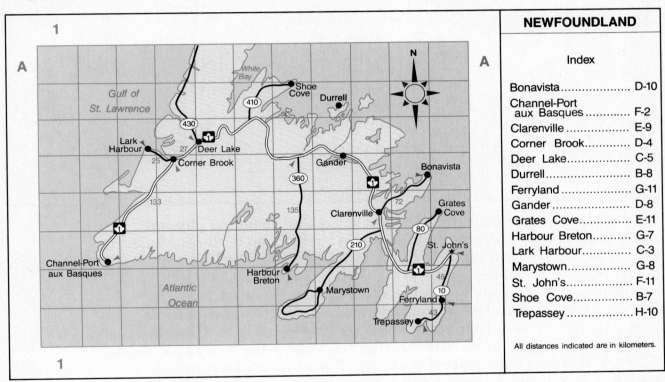

1. Complete the map grid by adding the missing letters and numbers.
2. Name each place described below.

   a. a city at the junction of Highways 1 and 430 _____

   b. a city 88 kilometers south of St. John's _____

   c. a city 25 kilometers northwest of Corner Brook _____

3. Where do you leave Highway 1 to go to Bonavista? _____
4. Which highways would take you from Harbour Breton to Shoe Cove?

_____

5 • Relief and Elevation

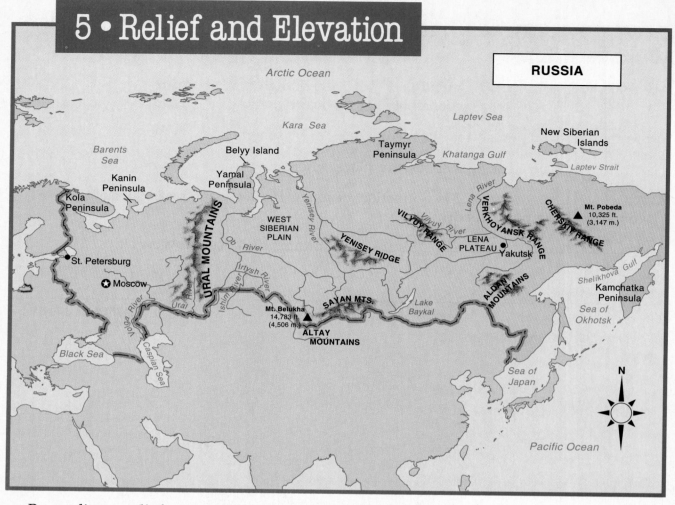

RUSSIA

By reading a **relief map** you can learn something about the physical features of a place. The map on this page is a relief map of Russia. Russia is now an independent country. It was formerly part of the Union of Soviet Socialist Republics.

Shading on relief maps shows the shape and height of the land. The highest, steepest mountain ranges have dark shading. Lower, less steep mountain ranges have lighter shading. Valleys and plains have no shading.

Besides mountains, relief maps usually show the major rivers of a place. A river's **source** is where it begins. A river flows downhill towards its **mouth**, where it empties into a sea or ocean. Many rivers flow into other rivers. These smaller rivers are called **tributaries**.

► Name a tributary of the Lena River.

► Name three rivers that flow north.

► Does the Ob River flow mainly through the low lands or high lands?

► In which mountain range are the sources of the Ural and Volga Rivers? These rivers empty into what sea?

► What is the longest mountain range in Russia?

► What other landforms are shown on this map?

► What other water forms are shown on this map?

► What mountain on this map is 10,325 feet high?

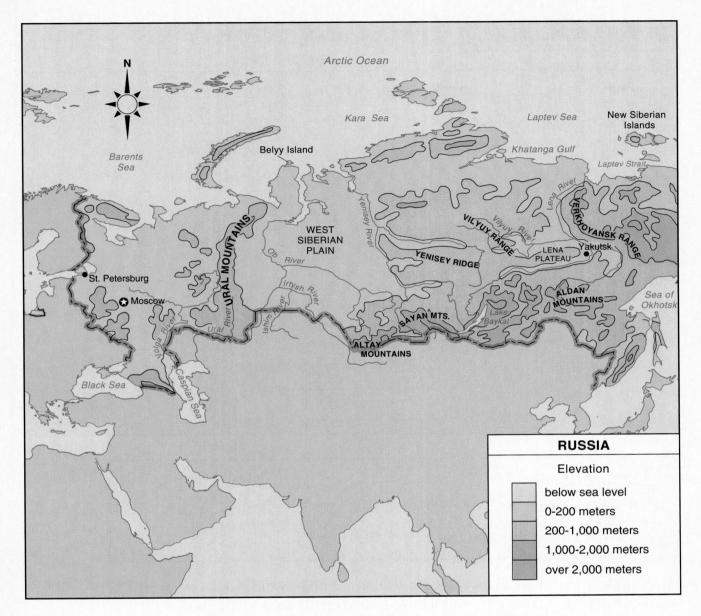

RUSSIA

Elevation

below sea level
0-200 meters
200-1,000 meters
1,000-2,000 meters
over 2,000 meters

This map shows part of Russia. Colors on the map show how high the land is, or its elevation. **Elevation** is the height of the land above or below the level of the sea. Read the legend to understand what elevation each color represents.

► What color shows the highest areas in Russia?

► What color shows the lowest areas?

Like a relief map, an elevation map gives a picture of how the land looks. An elevation map uses zones of color to show areas of land with similar elevation. A relief map gives an almost three-dimensional picture of the land. In what ways might we use relief and elevation maps?

► These places are in which elevation zones?
        Moscow   Lake Baykal   Yakutsk

► At what elevation is the source of the Ural River?

► Where in Russia is the elevation lowest?

Reading a Relief Map

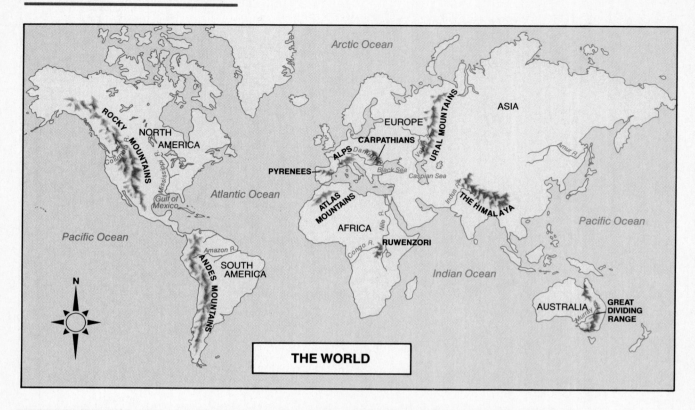

THE WORLD

☑ Map Attack!

✔ **Read the title.** This map shows _____.

   What is one thing to learn from this map? _____

1. Complete the chart below. Identify one mountain range and one river in each continent. Write the direction each river flows and the body of water into which it empties.

Continent	Mountain Range	River	Direction	Body of Water
a. North America	_____	_____	_____	_____
b. South America	_____	_____	_____	_____
c. Asia	_____	_____	_____	_____
d. Europe	_____	_____	_____	_____
e. Australia	_____	_____	_____	_____

2. Draw a conclusion. Rivers may flow north, south, east, or west. What determines the direction that a river flows?

_____

Reading an Elevation Map

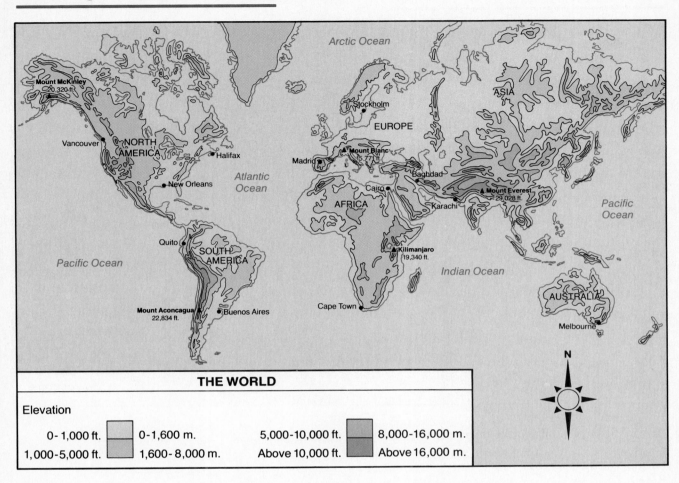

THE WORLD

Elevation

0- 1,000 ft.	0-1,600 m.	5,000-10,000 ft.	8,000-16,000 m.
1,000-5,000 ft.	1,600- 8,000 m.	Above 10,000 ft.	Above 16,000 m.

1. Circle the places in this list that are between 0 and 1,000 feet above sea level.

   New Orleans   Baghdad   Madrid   Cairo   Cape Town

   Karachi   Stockholm   Buenos Aires   Melbourne

2. Write the elevation and continent of these mountain peaks.

Mountain	Elevation	Continent
a. Aconcagua	_____	_____
b. Blanc	_____	_____
c. Everest	_____	_____
d. McKinley	_____	_____
e. Kilimanjaro	_____	_____

3. Draw a conclusion. The largest area of land over 10,000 feet above

   sea level is on which continent? _____

Reading a Map of Turkey

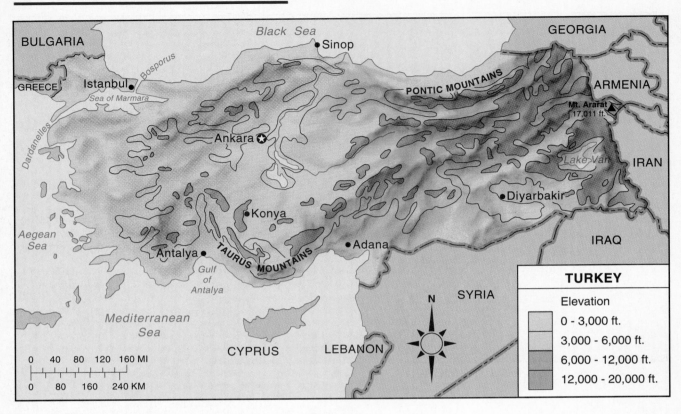

1. What mountain is shown on this map? _____

   How high is this mountain? _____

2. Identify the two mountain ranges shown on the map. For each one, identify the part of the country in which it is located.

   <u>Mountain Range</u>   <u>Part of Country</u>

   a. _____   _____

   b. _____   _____

3. Is the eastern or western part of Turkey more mountainous? _____

4. Does the elevation of the land increase or decrease as it approaches the

   coast? _____

5. About how far from Istanbul is Mt. Ararat? _____

6. About how far from Sinop is Adana? _____

7. Imagine you are traveling by boat from Antalya in southern Turkey to Sinop in northern Turkey. List four bodies of water you must cross.

   _____   _____

   _____   _____

Skill Check

Vocabulary Check   relief   elevation   mouth
                          tributary   source

Write the word that best completes each sentence.

1. A(n) _____ map uses shading to show mountains on a map.

2. A(n) _____ map uses zones of color to show the height of land.

3. A river's _____ is where it begins, and its _____ is where it empties into a sea or ocean.

4. A river that flows into a larger river is a _____.

Map Check

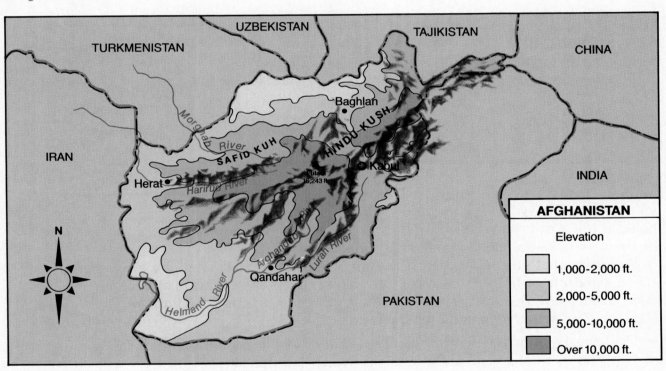

1. Name two tributaries of the Helmand River.

   _____

2. Name a river that flows through the Safid Kuh Mountains.

   _____

3. Name a river whose source is in the Hindu Kush Mountains.

   _____

4. Where are the areas of lowest elevation in Afghanistan?

   _____

6 • Latitude and Longitude

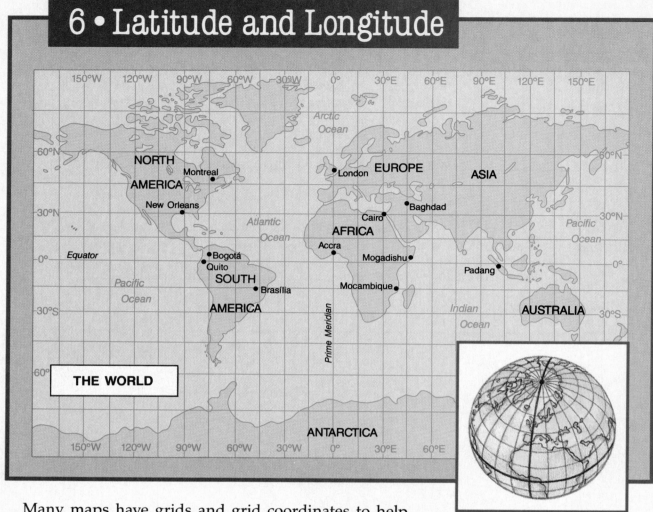

Many maps have grids and grid coordinates to help locate places. World maps and globes have grids on them. Look at the world map above. The grid pattern on the map is made up of **lines of latitude** and **lines of longitude**.

The lines that go east and west are the lines of latitude. They are also called **parallels** of latitude because they never touch each other. Latitude is used to measure distances north and south of the Equator. The Equator is 0° latitude. The symbol ° stands for **degrees**.

► Find the Equator on the map above. What cities lie near the Equator? Look north of the Equator to find 30° North latitude. What cities lie near 30° North latitude? Find 15° South latitude. What cities lie near 15° South latitude?

The lines that go north and south are the lines of longitude. They are also called **meridians** of longitude. Longitude is used to measure distances east and west of the **Prime Meridian**. The Prime Meridian is 0° longitude and goes from the North Pole to the South Pole. All lines of longitude meet at the North and South Poles.

► Find the Prime Meridian at 0° longitude. What cities lie near the Prime Meridian? Now look east of the Prime Meridian to find 45° East longitude. What cities lie near 45° East longitude? Find 75° West longitude. What cities lie near 75° West longitude?

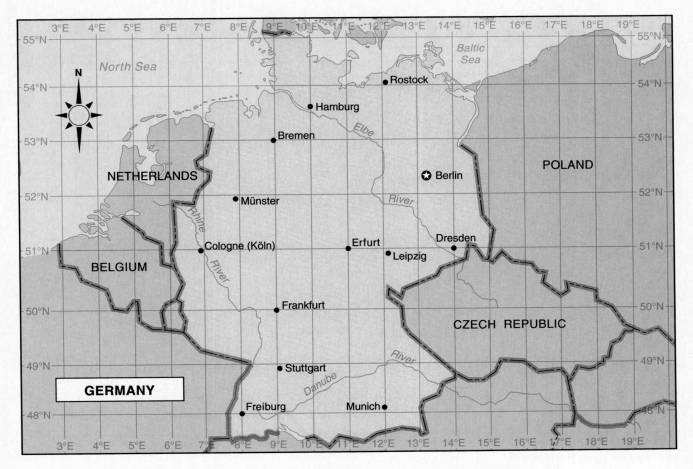

Look at the map of the world on page 34. You can see that the lines of latitude begin with 0° at the Equator and increase as they go north and south. The highest numbers are at the poles. The North Pole is 90° North latitude, and the South Pole is 90° South latitude.

The lines of longitude begin with 0° at the Prime Meridian and increase as they go east and west of the Prime Meridian. The highest number is 180°. The line of longitude directly opposite the Prime Meridian is 180°.

The lines of latitude and longitude form a grid pattern. This grid enables us to locate every place on Earth. Look at the map above. Find 51° North latitude. Run your finger along it until it crosses 7° East longitude. You have found the city of Cologne. The coordinates of Cologne are 51° North latitude and 7° East longitude, or 51°N, 7°E. Every spot on Earth has its own coordinates.

► Use latitude and longitude coordinates to find these places on the map. The coordinate for latitude is always named first.

Frankfurt	50°N, 9°E
Bremen	53°N, 9°E
Munich	48°N, 12°E

► Estimate the coordinates (latitude and longitude) of these places on the map:

        Münster
        Leipzig
        Stuttgart

Using Latitude and Longitude

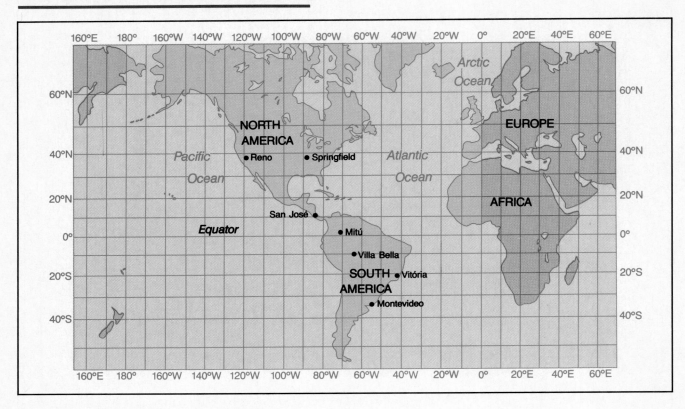

1. Trace the 70°W meridian in green.

   a. Is that line east or west of the Prime Meridian? _____
   b. Is most of the area shown on the map in the Eastern or Western

      Hemisphere? _____
2. Trace the Equator in red.
   Draw an N just north of the Equator.
   Draw an S just south of the Equator.
3. a. What city is near the place where the Equator and 70°W cross?

   _____

   b. What are its coordinates? _____, 70°W.
4. Find the missing coordinate for these cities.

   a. Springfield   40°N   , _____

   b. Vitória   _____,   40°W

   c. Reno   _____,   120°W

   d. San José   10°N   , _____

   e. Villa Bella   _____,   65°W

   f. Montevideo   35°S   , _____

Using Latitude and Longitude

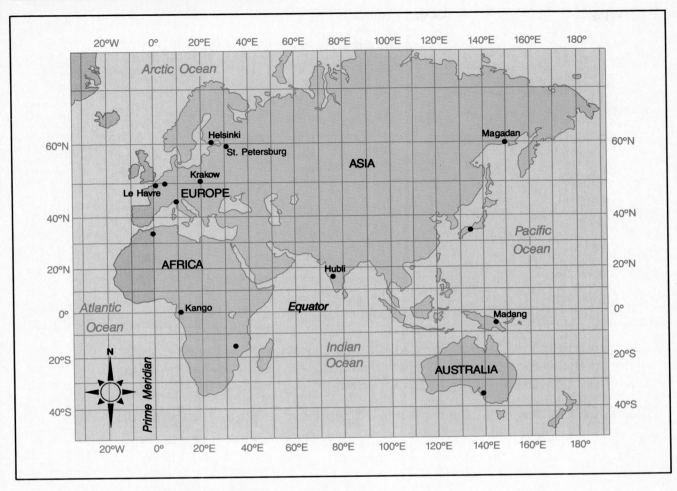

1. Label the cities at these locations on the map.
   a. 35° S, 140°E   Murray Bridge
   b. 50°N,   5°E   Namur
   c. 35°N, 135°E   Osaka
   d. 45°N, 10°E   Parma
   e. 15° S, 35°E   Zomba
   f. 35°N,   0°   Saida

2. Write the latitude and longitude coordinates of these cities.

	Latitude	Longitude
a. Helsinki	_____	_____
b. Le Havre	_____	_____
c. St. Petersburg	_____	_____
d. Madang	_____	_____
e. Krakow	_____	_____
f. Hubli	_____	_____

Tracking a Hurricane

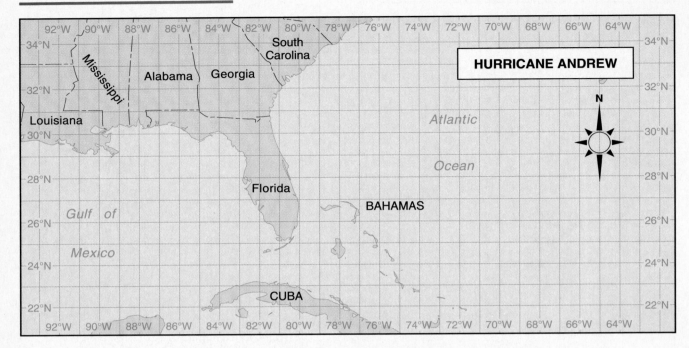

1. Use the latitude and longitude coordinates to track Hurricane Andrew's path on the map above. Put a dot on the map for each coordinate. Number each dot. Connect the dots to track Hurricane Andrew's path.

Position	Latitude	Longitude	Position	Latitude	Longitude
1	24°N	63°W	9	26°N	85°W
2	25°N	65°W	10	26½°N	87°W
3	26°N	69°W	11	27½°N	89°W
4	25½°N	72°W	12	29°N	91°W
5	25½°N	74°W	13	30°N	91½°W
6	25½°N	76½°W	14	31°N	91½°W
7	25½°N	79°W	15	31½°N	91°W
8	25½°N	81°W	16	32°N	90°W

2. Write the direction that Hurricane Andrew traveled

   a. from Position 1 to Position 3. _____

   b. from Position 4 to Position 8. _____

   c. from Position 9 to Position 13. _____

   d. from Position 14 to Position 16. _____

3. In what body of water did the hurricane begin? _____

4. What other body of water did it cross? _____

5. Where did Hurricane Andrew hit land?

   _____

Skill Check

Vocabulary Check   latitude   degrees   longitude
                                meridians   parallels   Prime Meridian

Write the word or phrase that best completes each sentence.

1. The _____ is the starting point for measuring distances east and west.

2. Lines of latitude, also called _____, measure distances north and south of the Equator.

3. Lines of longitude, also called _____, meet at the poles.

Map Check

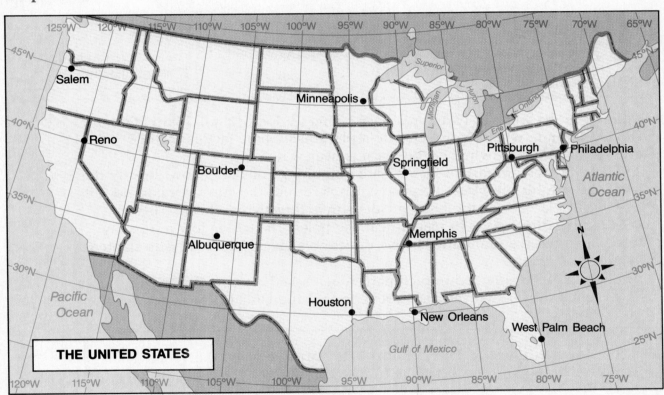

1. Name the cities at these locations.

   a. 40°N, 90°W _____   c. 40°N, 105°W _____

   b. 40°N, 75°W _____   d. 35°N, 90°W _____

2. Write the latitude and longitude coordinates of these cities.

                     Latitude   Longitude   Latitude   Longitude

   a. New Orleans _____ _____   c. Reno   _____ _____

   b. Pittsburgh   _____ _____   d. Houston _____ _____

7 • Climate Maps

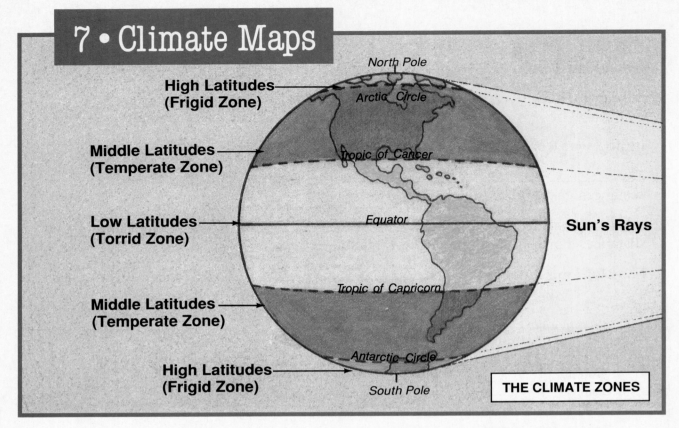

High Latitudes (Frigid Zone)

Middle Latitudes (Temperate Zone)

Low Latitudes (Torrid Zone)

Middle Latitudes (Temperate Zone)

High Latitudes (Frigid Zone)

North Pole
Arctic Circle
Tropic of Cancer
Equator
Tropic of Capricorn
Antarctic Circle
South Pole
Sun's Rays

THE CLIMATE ZONES

Climate is the weather of an area over a long period of time. Many different factors determine what kind of climate a place has. Some factors include elevation, winds, and whether the place is near water.

One of the most important factors in determining climate is how directly the rays of the sun hit the place. Because Earth is round, the sun's rays do not hit it evenly. In places near the Equator, the sun is directly overhead. These places receive direct rays. In places near the poles, the sun is low in the sky. These places receive slanted rays. The direct rays give more heat. The slanted rays give less heat.

The world can be divided into **climate zones** based on how directly the sun's rays strike Earth. Look at the map above to find the climate zones.

The **low latitudes,** or **Torrid Zone,** is the area between the Tropic of Cancer (23½°N) and the Tropic of Capricorn (23½°S). *Torrid* means "very hot." The sun's direct rays heat the Torrid Zone all year round.

The **high latitudes,** or **Frigid Zones,** cover the area between the Arctic Circle (66½°N) and the North Pole (90°N) and the area between the Antarctic Circle (66½°S) and the South Pole (90°S). *Frigid* means "very cold." The sun is low in the sky in these areas, so only slanted rays hit them. As a result, these zones are cold all year.

The **middle latitudes,** or **Temperate Zones,** are between the Torrid Zone and the Frigid Zones. *Temperate* means "balanced." The climate in the Temperate Zones is a balance between the heat of the Torrid Zone and the cold of the Frigid Zones. The climate of places in the Temperate Zones changes from season to season.

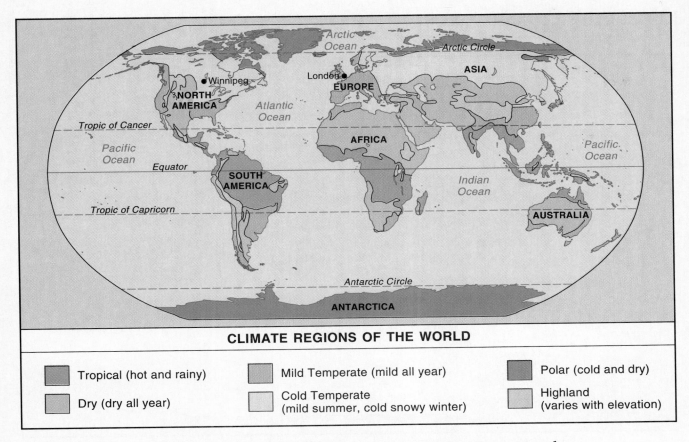

CLIMATE REGIONS OF THE WORLD

■ Tropical (hot and rainy)

■ Dry (dry all year)

■ Mild Temperate (mild all year)

■ Cold Temperate
(mild summer, cold snowy winter)

■ Polar (cold and dry)

■ Highland
(varies with elevation)

Not all places within a climate zone have the same climate. For example, Winnipeg, Canada, and London, England, are both in the Temperate Zone. The rays of sunlight that strike Winnipeg are about as direct as the ones that strike London. Yet the two places have very different climates. London has a much warmer climate because it is near the sea. This is an example of how factors other than sunlight affect the climate of a place.

To reflect differences within climate zones, a list of **climate regions** has been developed. There are six basic climate regions. As you read about the climate regions of the world, locate them on the map above.

The **tropical climate** is hot and rainy. Much of the world's rain forests and jungles grow in tropical climates.

Areas that have a **dry climate** are dry all year round. Much of the western United States has a dry climate. So does northern Africa, where the great Sahara desert is.

The **mild temperate climate** is mild all year.

Areas with **cold temperate climates** have mild summers, but the winters are cold and snowy.

Areas with a **polar climate** are cold and dry.

► Find the polar climates on the map. Why do you think this climate has the name it does?

Mountainous areas have a **highland climate**, which varies with the elevation.

Every place on Earth has one of these six climate regions. Find where you live on the map. In which climate region do you live?

Mastering Climate Zones

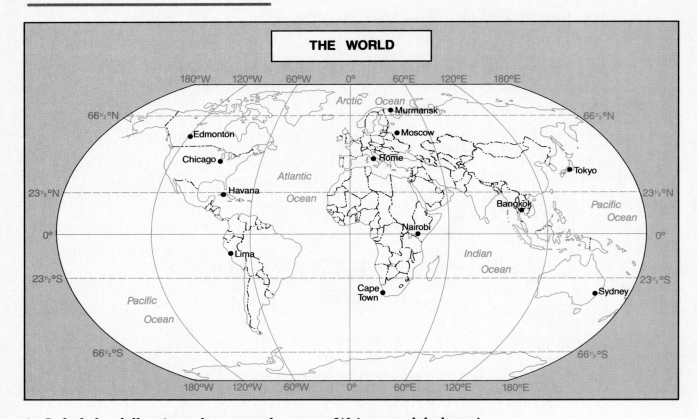

1. Label the following places on the map. Write two labels twice.

Equator	Tropic of Cancer	Arctic Circle	Frigid Zone
Antarctic Circle	Tropic of Capricorn	Torrid Zone	Temperate Zone

2. Lightly color the Torrid Zone orange, the Temperate Zones yellow, and the Frigid Zones blue.

3. After each city below, write its climate zone. Then write whether it is in the high, middle, or low latitudes.

Place	Climate Zone	Latitudes
a. Murmansk	_____	_____
b. Chicago	_____	_____
c. Cape Town	_____	_____
d. Nairobi	_____	_____
e. Tokyo	_____	_____
f. Havana	_____	_____
g. Rome	_____	_____
h. Bangkok	_____	_____
i. Lima	_____	_____

Reading a Climate Map

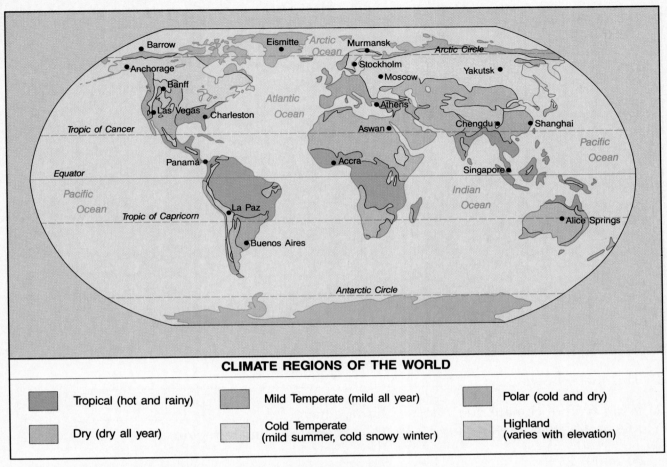

CLIMATE REGIONS OF THE WORLD

- Tropical (hot and rainy)
- Dry (dry all year)
- Mild Temperate (mild all year)
- Cold Temperate (mild summer, cold snowy winter)
- Polar (cold and dry)
- Highland (varies with elevation)

This map shows six climate regions of the world.

Write the name of three cities in each climate region.

1. Tropical _____ _____ _____

2. Dry _____ _____ _____

3. Mild Temperate _____ _____ _____

4. Cold Temperate _____ _____ _____

5. Polar _____ _____ _____

6. Highland _____ _____ _____

7. Which climate is found mostly in the Frigid Zone? _____

8. The tropical region is found mostly in what climate zone? _____

9. Draw a conclusion. Which has the most areas with cold snowy winters, the Northern or the Southern Hemisphere?

_____

Reading a Climate Map of Europe

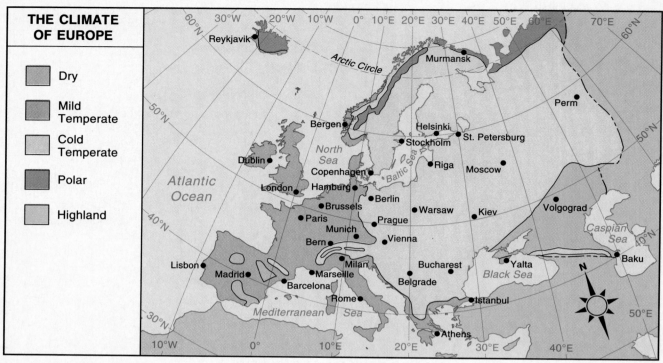

THE CLIMATE OF EUROPE

- Dry
- Mild Temperate
- Cold Temperate
- Polar
- Highland

1. This map shows _____.

2. What type of climate does most of Europe have? _____

3. Name the cities at these locations. Then write the climate region.

   a. 60°N, 25°E   _____   _____

   b. 50°N, 45°E   _____   _____

   c. 60°N, 5°E   _____   _____

   d. 45°N, 20°E   _____   _____

   e. 55°N, 5°W   _____   _____

4. Estimate the degrees latitude and longitude of each city. Then write its climate region.

	Latitude	Longitude	Climate Region
a. St. Petersburg	_____	_____	_____
b. Kiev	_____	_____	_____
c. London	_____	_____	_____
d. Baku	_____	_____	_____
e. Madrid	_____	_____	_____

5. Polar regions on this map do not extend below what line of latitude? _____

Skill Check

Vocabulary Check   **Torrid Zone**   **high latitudes**   **climate**
                       Temperate Zone **middle latitudes**
                       Frigid Zone   **low latitudes**

Write the word or phrase that best completes each sentence.

1. The Temperate Zone is found in the _____.

2. The area between the Tropic of Cancer and the Tropic of Capricorn

   is called the _____, or _____.

3. The high latitudes are also called the _____.

4. The weather of an area over a long period of time is its _____.

Map Check

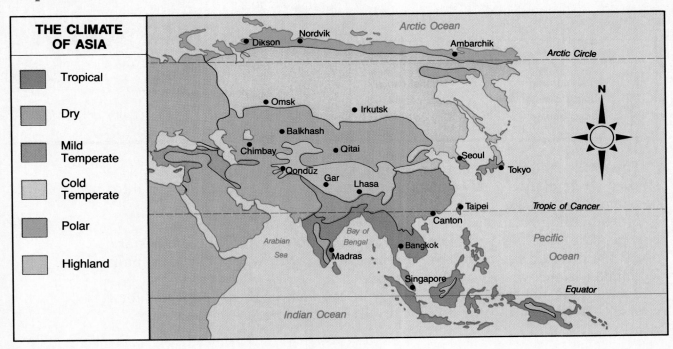

1. Write the names of three cities in each climate region.

   a. Tropical   _____   _____   _____

   b. Dry   _____   _____   _____

   c. Mild Temperate _____   _____   _____

   d. Cold Temperate _____   _____   _____

   e. Polar   _____   _____   _____

   f. Highland   _____   _____   _____

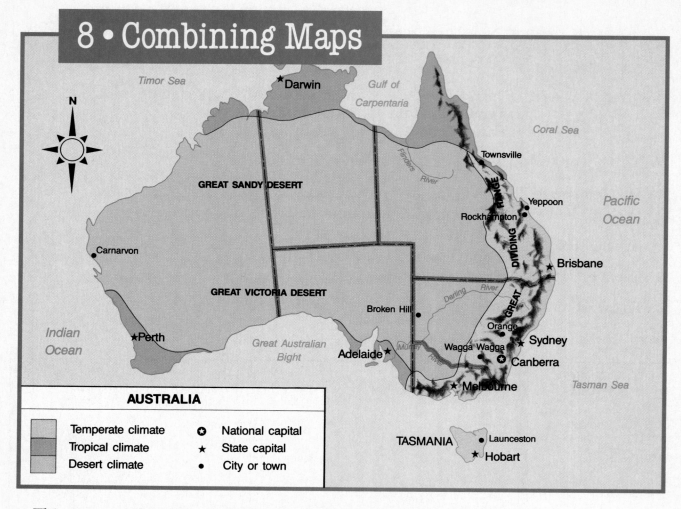

8 • Combining Maps

This map combines facts from several kinds of maps you have already studied. It combines a relief map, a climate map, and a political map into one map of Australia.

By combining many facts on a map, we can look for **relationships** between the facts. Does climate have anything to do with where cities are built? Do physical features have anything to do with where cities are built? Do climate zones change with elevation?

By studying the facts on this map, you can answer these questions for yourself. By comparing the facts you will be able to see Australia more clearly.

Read the Facts

► What and where are the seas, gulfs, and oceans that surround Australia?

► What and where are Australia's main mountain range and deserts?

► Where are Australia's temperate, tropical, and desert climates?

Draw Conclusions

► In what climate zone are most of Australia's cities?

► Near what physical features are most of Australia's cities?

► Where in Australia do very few people live? Why do few people live there?

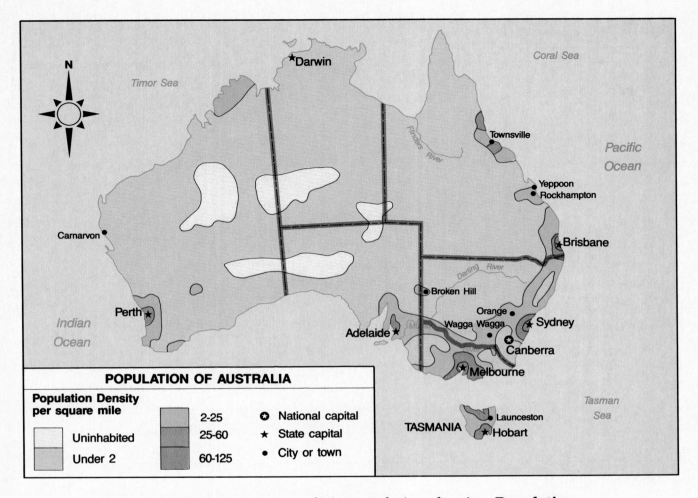

POPULATION OF AUSTRALIA

Population Density per square mile

Uninhabited	2-25
Under 2	25-60
	60-125

✪ National capital
★ State capital
● City or town

The map on this page shows Australia's population density. **Population density** is how many people live in a square mile. Parts of Australia are uninhabited, no one lives there. The darkest colors on the map stand for the places with the densest (most crowded) population. Find the area around Sydney, Australia's biggest city.

Read the key to learn what the purple color stands for. Closest to Sydney there are between 60 and 125 people living in each square mile. Point to Sydney, then move your finger inland (west or northwest). As you move away from the main part of the city, the population becomes less and less dense.

Read the Facts

► What are the five most densely populated places in Australia?

Compare the Maps Compare the facts on the map on this page and the map on page 46 to answer the questions.

► What is the population density in Australia's desert regions?

► What is the population density in the mountain region?

► What is the population density in the regions with mild temperate climates?

Draw a Conclusion

► On the whole, which climate does Australia's population prefer?

Reading a Combined Map

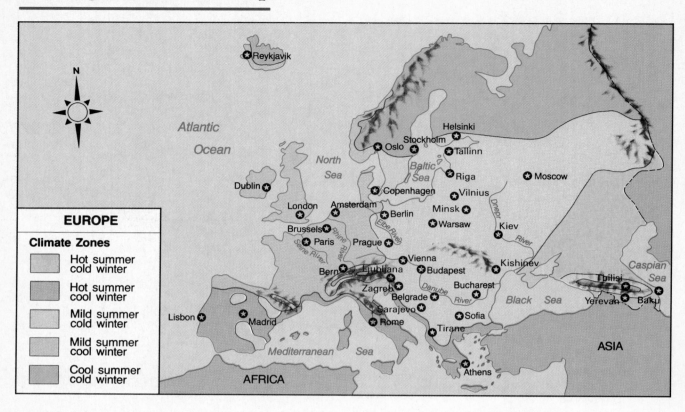

EUROPE

Climate Zones

- Hot summer cold winter
- Hot summer cool winter
- Mild summer cold winter
- Mild summer cool winter
- Cool summer cold winter

☑ Map Attack!

- ✔ **Read the title.** This map shows _____.
- ✔ **Read the compass rose.** Label the intermediate direction arrows.

1. What information is combined on this map?

   _____

2. Name one major water form near each of these climate zones.

   a. mild summer, cold winter _____

   b. hot summer, cold winter _____

   c. mild summer, cool winter _____

3. Name two cities in each of these climate zones.

   a. hot summer, cool winter _____

   b. mild summer, cool winter _____

   c. mild summer, cold winter _____

4. Find the Danube River. Name the capital cities that are along the

   Danube River. _____

Reading a Combined Map

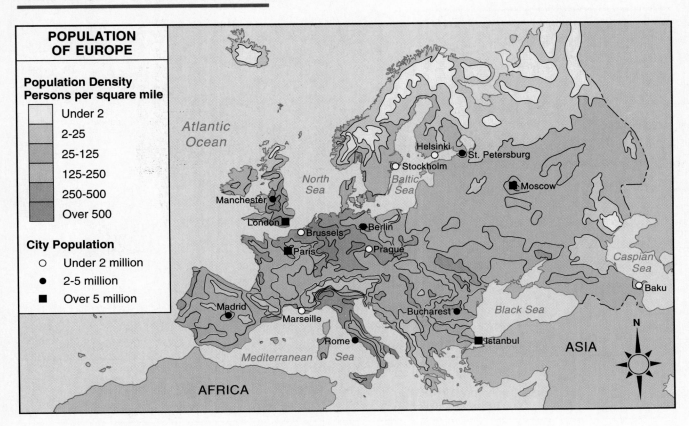

POPULATION OF EUROPE

Population Density
Persons per square mile

- Under 2
- 2-25
- 25-125
- 125-250
- 250-500
- Over 500

City Population
- ○ Under 2 million
- ● 2-5 million
- ■ Over 5 million

1. Name four cities that have more than 5 million people.

   _____

2. Name six cities that have 2 to 5 million people.

   _____

   _____

3. Name six cities that have less than 2 million people.

   _____

   _____

4. Is the population density higher or lower around the cities? _____

   Why do you think this is so? _____

5. What is the population density of most of the areas around the Baltic

   Sea? _____

6. Draw a conclusion. Look at the map on page 48. What climate zone has

   the lowest population density? _____

   Why do you think this is so? _____

Reading a Combined Map

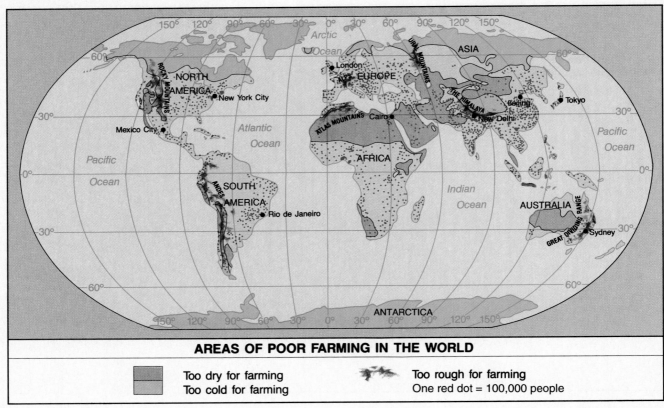

AREAS OF POOR FARMING IN THE WORLD

Too dry for farming
Too cold for farming

Too rough for farming
One red dot = 100,000 people

1. What two continents have the largest area of land too dry for farming?

   _____

2. What continent is completely without a settled population?

   _____

3. What continent is too cold for farming? _____

4. What continent has the most areas of dense population? _____

5. Label the following places on the map.

   <u>Sahara Desert</u> an area in northern Africa too dry for farming
   <u>Gobi Desert</u> an area north of the Himalaya too dry for farming
   <u>Kalahari Desert</u> an area in southern Africa too dry for farming
   <u>Great Victoria Desert</u> an area in western Australia too dry for farming

6. Draw a conclusion. Name three conditions that make land bad for
   farming. Then name one place in the world that fits each condition.

   <u>Condition</u>   <u>Place</u>

   _____   _____

   _____   _____

   _____   _____

Vocabulary Check   relationships   population density

Write the word or phrase that best completes the sentence.

1. The number of people per square mile is _____.

2. You can find _____ when you combine or compare facts.

Map Check

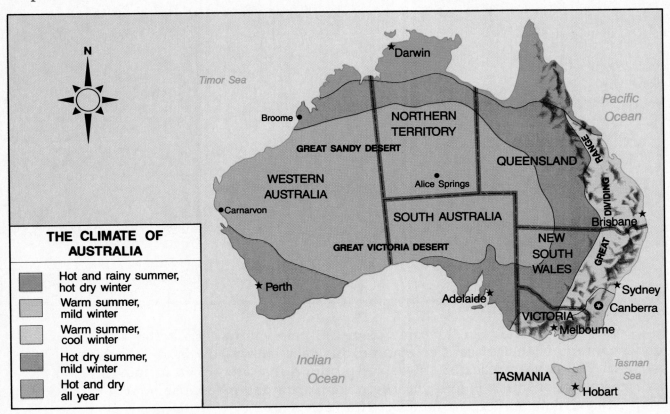

THE CLIMATE OF AUSTRALIA

Hot and rainy summer, hot dry winter

Warm summer, mild winter

Warm summer, cool winter

Hot dry summer, mild winter

Hot and dry all year

1. What is the climate of these cities?

   a. Sydney _____

   b. Darwin _____

   c. Alice Springs _____

   d. Perth _____

2. What is the climate of Tasmania? _____

3. How is the climate east of the Great Dividing Range different from

   the climate west of it? _____

4. Which state has the least variety in climate? _____

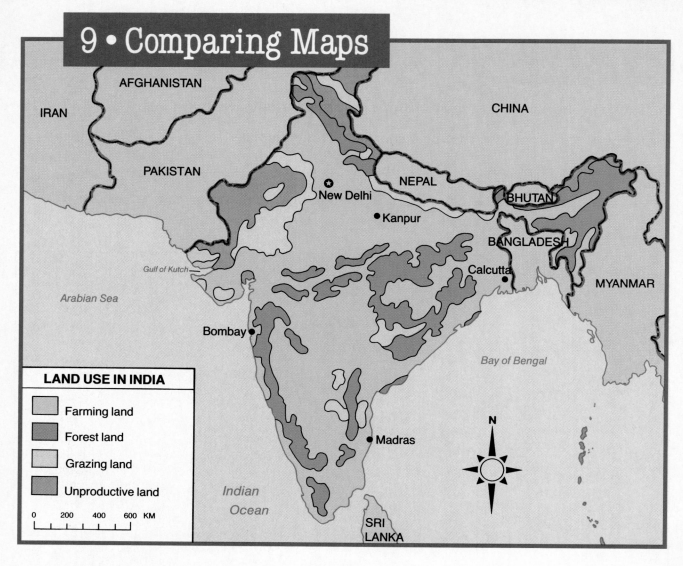

9 • Comparing Maps

LAND USE IN INDIA

- Farming land
- Forest land
- Grazing land
- Unproductive land

0   200   400   600 KM

Comparing two maps of the same place can help you to get a better understanding of that place. The map on this page shows how land is used in India. The map on page 53 shows the products that are grown or mined in each region of India. Before you begin comparing the maps, use your **Map Attack!** skills to become familiar with each map.

> ✔ **Read the title.** What can you expect to learn from each map?
> ✔ **Read the legend.** Find an example of each land use on this map.
>   Find an example of each resource on the next map.
> ✔ **Read the compass rose.** Find north on each map.
> ✔ **Read the scale.** Are distances measured in miles or kilometers?
>   Is the scale the same on the maps?

After you are familiar with each map, study each map separately to see what you can learn. Read the facts on each map.

► India's unproductive land is mostly in which region?

► India's northeast region is mostly used for what?

► What is the most widespread land use in India?

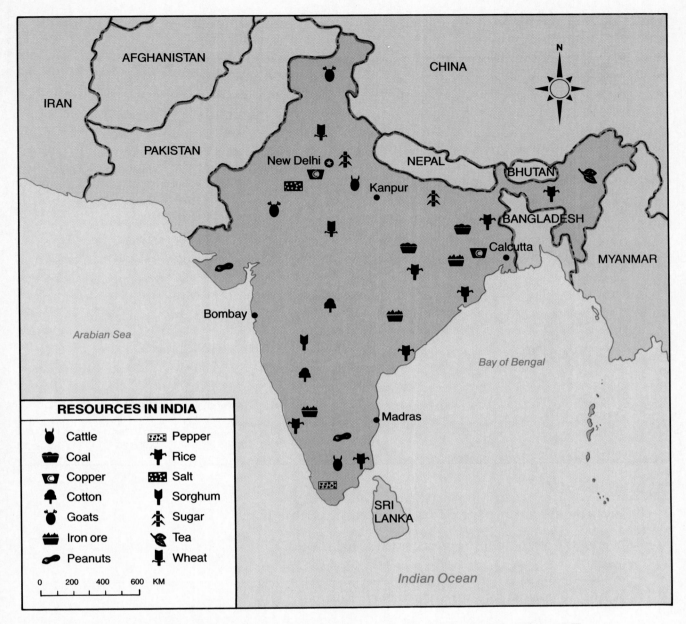

RESOURCES IN INDIA

Cattle		Pepper	
Coal		Rice	
Copper		Salt	
Cotton		Sorghum	
Goats		Sugar	
Iron ore		Tea	
Peanuts		Wheat	

0   200   400   600   KM

Once you are familiar with each map, you can begin comparing them. To compare land use and resources in the southern tip of India, first find the southern tip of India on each map. Make sure you are looking at the same area of India on each map. Is the pepper from southern India found in forest or farm land?

Now compare other areas of India. Use the legend of each map to help you answer these questions.

► What is the land use in most coal-mining areas of India?

► What is the land use in the area where goats are a product?

► What is the land use where salt is mined?

► What is the land use around each of these manufacturing centers?

       Calcutta   Bombay   Madras   New Delhi

► What resources are found near those manufacturing centers?

Comparing Maps

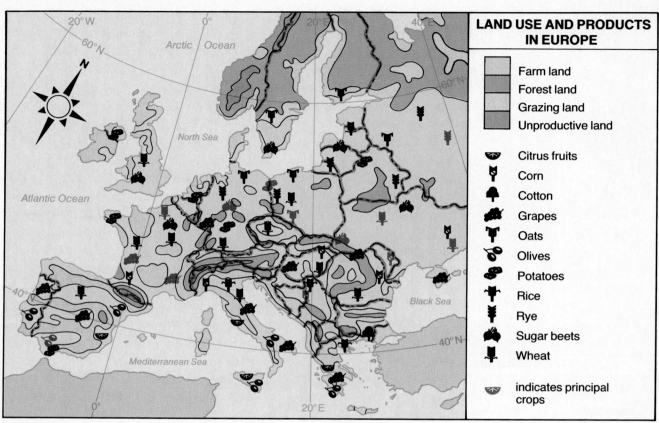

LAND USE AND PRODUCTS IN EUROPE

- Farm land
- Forest land
- Grazing land
- Unproductive land

- Citrus fruits
- Corn
- Cotton
- Grapes
- Oats
- Olives
- Potatoes
- Rice
- Rye
- Sugar beets
- Wheat

- indicates principal crops

☑ Map Attack!

Follow the steps on page 52 to begin reading this map.

1. What are the principal crops in southern Europe?

_____

2. What are the principal crops in eastern Europe?

_____

3. What is the main land use in Europe north of 60°N?

_____

4. Where are Europe's largest forests? _____

5. What is the main land use north of the Black Sea?

_____

6. Circle the crops most often grown where grapes are grown.

     rye   cotton   oats   olives   citrus fruits   corn   wheat

7. Circle the crops most often grown where wheat is grown.

    sugar beets   rye   oats   cotton   potatoes   olives   grapes

Comparing Maps

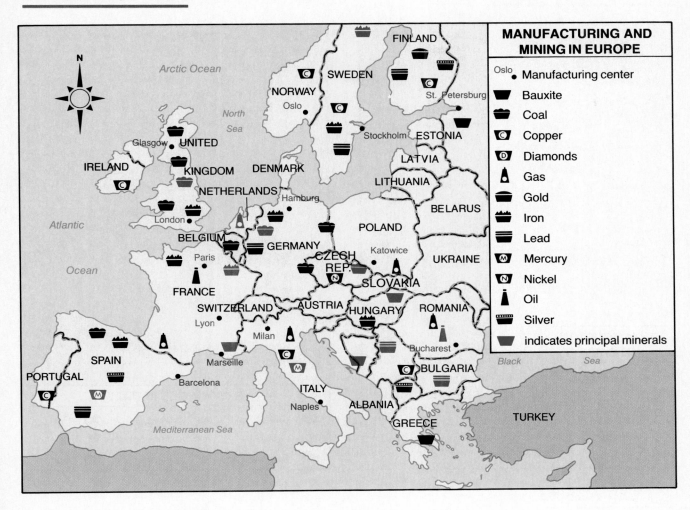

MANUFACTURING AND MINING IN EUROPE

Symbol	Meaning
Oslo •	Manufacturing center
	Bauxite
	Coal
Ⓒ	Copper
Ⓓ	Diamonds
	Gas
	Gold
	Iron
	Lead
Ⓜ	Mercury
Ⓝ	Nickel
	Oil
	Silver
	indicates principal minerals

1. Name five manufacturing centers in southern Europe.

   _____

2. Name five manufacturing centers in northern Europe.

   _____

3. Circle the principal crops and minerals in each of these countries.

   a. France   bauxite   grapes   gold   wheat   iron

   b. Spain   oats   olives   mercury   grapes   gas

   c. Italy   copper   rice   oil   corn   mercury

4. List the mining and farming industries in each of these countries.

   a. Greece   _____

   b. Italy   _____

   c. Hungary   _____

Comparing Maps

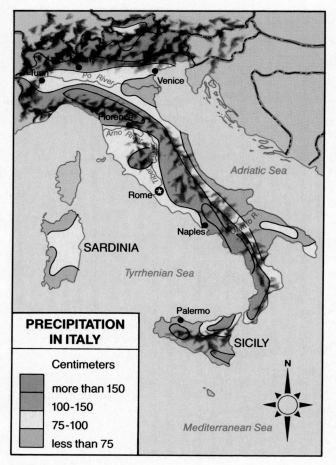

PRECIPITATION IN ITALY

Centimeters

- more than 150
- 100-150
- 75-100
- less than 75

RESOURCES IN ITALY

Coal	Hogs	Poultry
Goats	Lumber	Sheep
Grapes	Olives	Sulfur

☑ Map Attack!

Follow the steps on page 52 to preview the maps.

1. Circle the resources that are found near each city.

   a. Rome   olives   lumber   hogs   sheep   coal

   b. Florence   goats   olives   sheep   grapes   hogs

   c. Turin   sheep   coal   grapes   poultry   olives

2. Name three resources found along the Po River.

   _____

3. Name three resources found mostly in the mountains.

   _____

4. Name two resources found mostly in drier areas. _____

5. Name three resources found in the rainy area of northern Italy.

   _____

Skill Check

Vocabulary Check   comparing

Circle the best ending for the following sentence.

Comparing two different maps of the same place is

    a. necessary for you to determine directions.

    b. a good way to help you understand the place.

    c. the only way to learn about a country's products.

Map Check

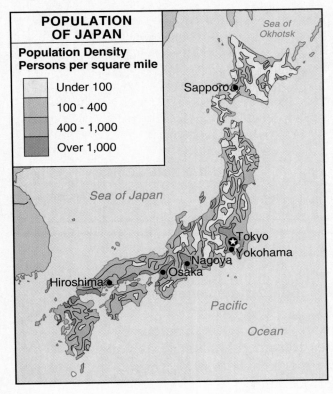

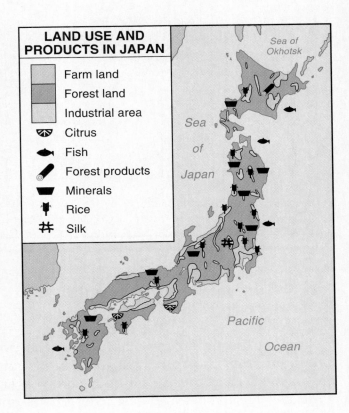

1. a. The map on the left shows _____.

    b. The map on the right shows _____.

2. Is the population density of Japan higher along the coasts or inland?

    _____

3. What is Japan's chief crop? _____

4. Does Japan have more farm land or forest land? _____

5. Is the population density of Japan higher in the farming areas or the

    industrial areas? _____

6. What products are found near Sapporo? _____

10 • Time Zones

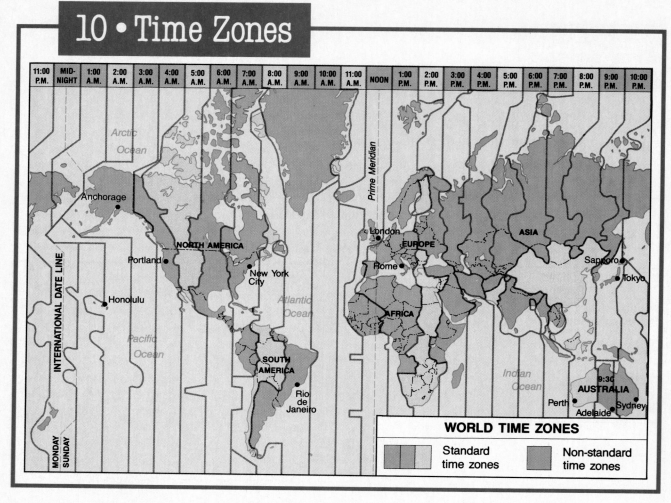

| 11:00 P.M. | MID-NIGHT | 1:00 A.M. | 2:00 A.M. | 3:00 A.M. | 4:00 A.M. | 5:00 A.M. | 6:00 A.M. | 7:00 A.M. | 8:00 A.M. | 9:00 A.M. | 10:00 A.M. | 11:00 A.M. | NOON | 1:00 P.M. | 2:00 P.M. | 3:00 P.M. | 4:00 P.M. | 5:00 P.M. | 6:00 P.M. | 7:00 P.M. | 8:00 P.M. | 9:00 P.M. | 10:00 P.M. |

WORLD TIME ZONES

Standard time zones   Non-standard time zones

Earth makes one complete turn, or rotation, every 24 hours. Since only half of Earth receives light from the sun at a time, it is not the same time everywhere on Earth. Earth is divided into 24 **standard time zones**, one time zone for each hour in the day.

Look at the time zone map above. The time in each zone is different by one hour from the zone next to it. Earth rotates toward the east. So as you travel west, the time is one hour earlier every time you cross into a new time zone. As you travel east, the time is one hour later.

Find London on the Prime Meridian (0 degrees). It is in the time zone labeled NOON. Now find Rome. It is one time zone east of London, so the time is one hour later. When it is 12:00 noon in London, it is 1:00 P.M. in Rome. Now find Rio de Janeiro. It is three time zones west of London, so the time is three hours earlier. When it is 12:00 noon in London, it is 9:00 A.M. in Rio de Janeiro.

Find New York City. How many time zones is it from London? Which direction is it from London? What time is it in New York City when it is 12:00 noon in London? It is 7 A.M. in New York City.

Notice that the time zones often follow political boundaries. This keeps places in one state, country, or area all in the same time zone. Some places around the world do not observe standard time zones and use different times. Find central Australia on the map. Notice that in Adelaide it is 9:30 when it is 8:00 in Perth.

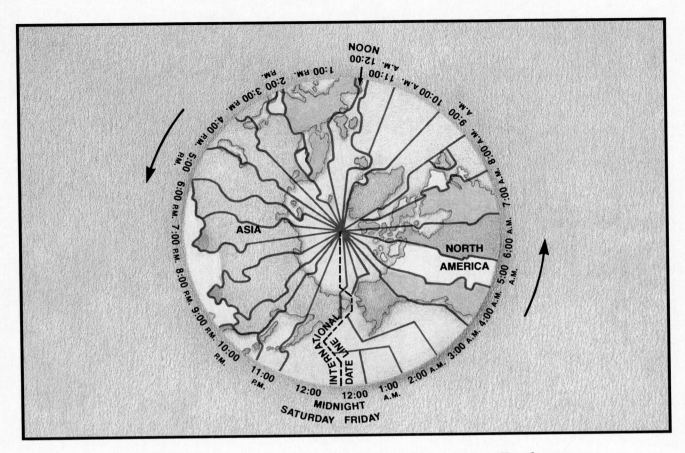

Remember that it takes 24 hours for Earth to rotate, and that Earth rotates toward the east. If you traveled west around Earth for 24 hours, you would set your watch back every time you entered a new time zone. When you arrived at home, your watch would show the same hour as when you left. But it would actually be 24 hours later—the next day.

Find the **International Date Line** on the drawing above. This imaginary line, at about 180° longitude, separates one day from the next. The time of day is the same on both sides of the line. But west of the line it is one day later than it is to the east. If it is midnight Sunday on the east side of the line, it is midnight Monday on the west side of the line.

Notice that the International Date Line does not follow the 180° line of longitude exactly. It goes around various countries to keep places in one political area in the same time zone and day.

Find Portland, Oregon, on the map on page 58. Suppose you start traveling west from Portland at 4:00 A.M. Friday morning. It is midnight at the Date Line. On the east side it is midnight Friday. But on the west side it is midnight Saturday. After you cross the Date Line, you enter late Saturday night. You actually miss one day, almost all of Friday. Farther west of the Date Line it is late evening on Saturday. In Sapporo it is 9:00 P.M. Saturday.

► Asia is west of the International Date Line. North America is east of the International Date Line. Look at the drawing above. If it is Monday in Asia, what day is it in North America?

► Look at the map on page 58. If it is 3:00 P.M. on Tuesday in Anchorage, Alaska, what is the day and time in Sydney, Australia?

Reading a Time Zone Map

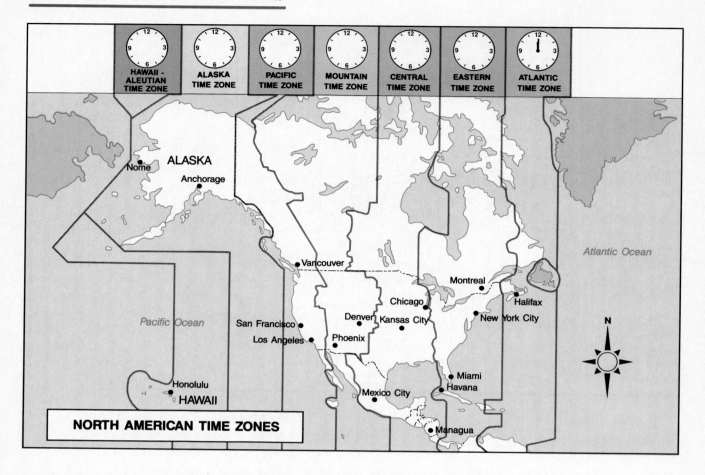

1. Lightly color the time zones. Match the colors at the top of the map. Follow the lines along state boundaries or physical features.

2. It is 12:00 noon in the Atlantic Time Zone. Write the correct times on the clocks for the other time zones. Remember, the time is one hour earlier as you travel west.

3. If it is 8:00 A.M. in Los Angeles, what time is it in each city listed below?

   a. Vancouver _____   e. Miami _____

   b. Kansas City _____   f. Denver _____

   c. Honolulu _____   g. New York City _____

   d. Anchorage _____   h. Halifax _____

4. The World Series is at 6:00 P.M. in New York City. What time is it in each city listed below?

   a. Montreal _____   d. Phoenix _____

   b. Mexico City _____   e. San Francisco _____

   c. Nome _____   f. Honolulu _____

Mastering World Time Zones

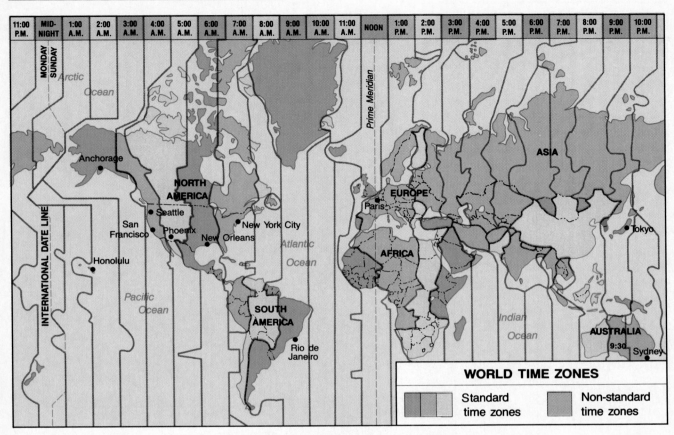

1. Which continents have a large area without standard time? Look at the colors in the map key.

   _____

2. How many time zones does each of these continents have?

   a. Africa _____   b. South America _____

3. If you go from Tokyo to Sydney, how many time zones do you cross?

   _____

4. If you go from Seattle to Rio de Janeiro, how many time zones do

   you cross? _____

5. If you go from Honolulu to New Orleans, how many time zones do

   you cross? _____

6. It is 7:00 A.M. in Phoenix. What time is it in Paris? _____

7. It is 3:00 P.M. in Rio de Janeiro. What time is it in San Francisco?

   _____

8. Suppose you fly from Anchorage to New York City. Do you move

   your watch ahead or back?_____ How many hours? _____

Mastering World Time Zones

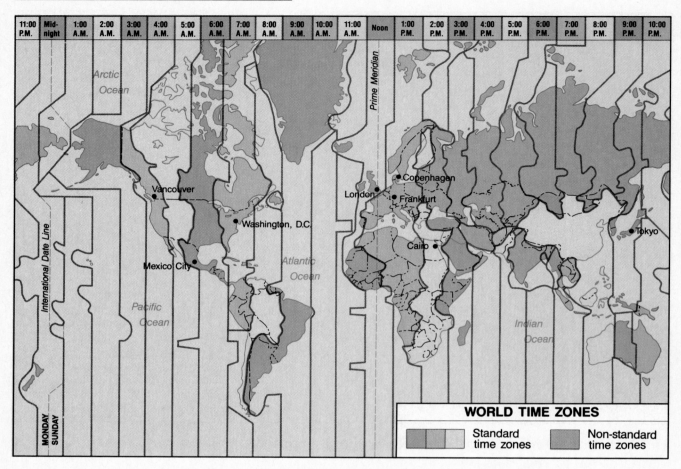

1. You are planning trips from London to various places around the world. Finish the chart below. Write the direction from London to each city. Then write whether you set your watch ahead (+) or back (−), and by how many hours. The first one is done for you.

From London to	Direction	Set Watch	How Many Hours
a. Frankfurt	east	+	1
b. Cairo	_____	___	___
c. Tokyo	_____	___	___
d. Mexico City	_____	___	___
e. Washington, D.C.	_____	___	___
f. Copenhagen	_____	___	___
g. Vancouver	_____	___	___

2. If it is 12:01 P.M. Tuesday in Frankfurt, what time and day is it halfway around the world? _____

Skill Check

Vocabulary Check   **standard time zones**   **International Date Line**

Write the words that best complete each sentence.

1. Earth has 24 _____ .

2. When you go west across the _____
   it is suddenly tomorrow, and you lose a day.

Map Check

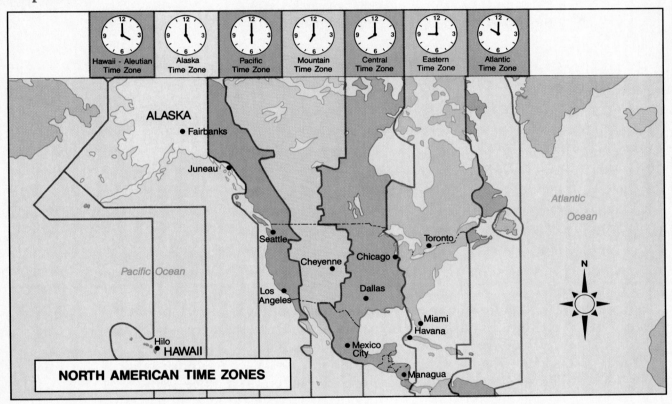

1. Dallas is in the _____ Time Zone.

2. Seattle is in the _____ Time Zone.

3. Toronto is in the _____ Time Zone.

4. Fairbanks is in the _____ Time Zone.

5. The President gave a speech at 9:00 P.M. Eastern Time. What time was it
   in these cities?

   a. Los Angeles _____   d. Havana _____

   b. Chicago _____   e. Cheyenne _____

   c. Hilo _____   f. Juneau _____

11 • Projections

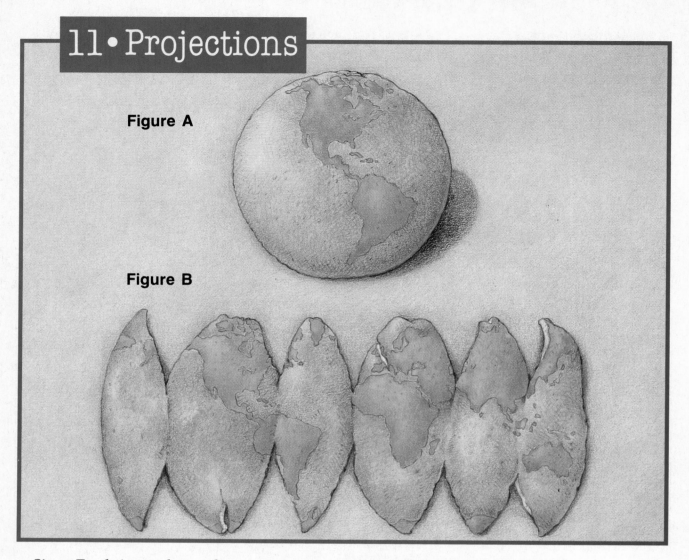

Figure A

Figure B

Since Earth is a sphere, the most accurate model of Earth is a globe. But often it is more useful to have a flat map of Earth. **Cartographers**—people who make maps—have made many flat maps of Earth.

Making a flat map of spherical Earth is not an easy task. To understand why, look at Figure A, which shows an orange made into a globe. Now imagine peeling the curved surface off the orange and making it lie flat. To do this, you need to stretch and tear the orange peel. Figure B shows the results. This action—taking a curved surface and forcing it to lie flat—is exactly what cartographers have to do when they make a flat map of the curved surface of Earth.

Look at the illustrations again. Notice how the shapes of the continents were changed when the curved peel was stretched flat. This change in a curved surface when it is flattened is called **distortion**. Every map of Earth has distortion. To draw a flat map of spherical Earth, parts of the sphere must be distorted, just as the orange peel must be distorted to make it lie flat.

Different maps distort Earth in different ways. Some maps distort the shape of continents. Other maps distort the size. The type of distortion a map has depends on its projection. A **projection** is the way in which a cartographer projects, or shows, the curved surface of Earth on a flat map. A cartographer chooses the type of projection to use based on the purpose of the map.

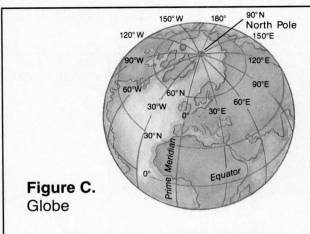

Figure C.
Globe

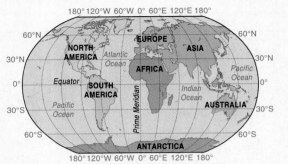

Figure E. Robinson Projection

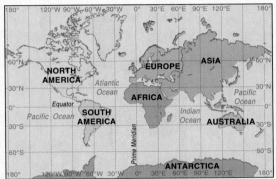

Figure D. Mercator Projection

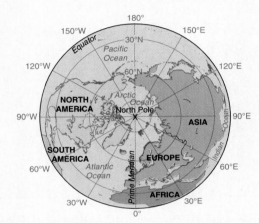

Figure F. North Polar Projection

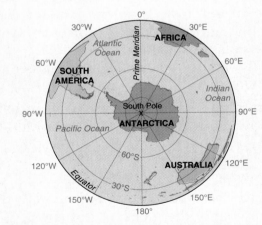

Figure G. South Polar Projection

There are many different kinds of map projections. A few of the most common ones are pictured here.

Look first at the drawing of the globe in Figure C. It shows the grid lines of latitude and longitude. As you look at each map projection, compare the grid on it with the grid on the drawing of the globe. This will help you see how each projection distorts the surface of Earth.

The map in Figure D is a **Mercator projection**. It is named after Gerhardus Mercator, a Flemish cartographer who lived in the 1500s. The Mercator projection is one of the most common map projections.

The map in Figure E is a **Robinson projection**. It is named after the American cartographer Arthur Robinson. This projection is becoming more popular.

The maps in Figures F and G are **polar projections**. Why do you think these projections are called polar projections?

► Turn to the world map on page 62. What type of projection is it?

► Turn to the world map on page 50. What type of projection is it?

Reading a Mercator Projection

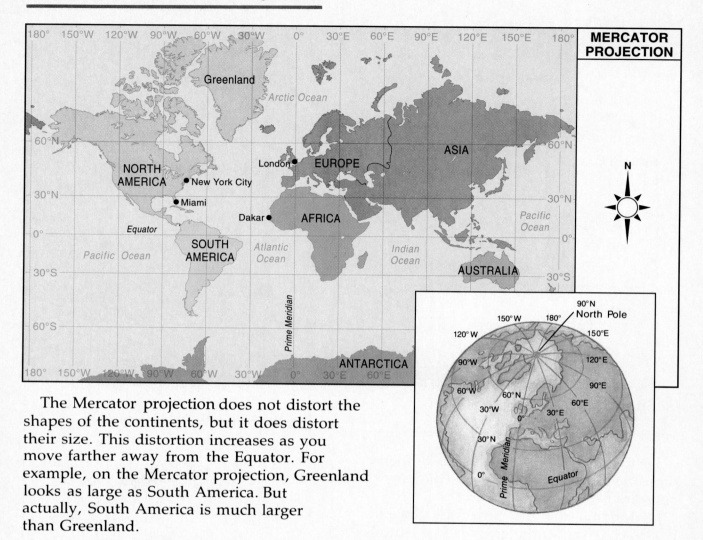

The Mercator projection does not distort the shapes of the continents, but it does distort their size. This distortion increases as you move farther away from the Equator. For example, on the Mercator projection, Greenland looks as large as South America. But actually, South America is much larger than Greenland.

1. Trace these meridians in green on both the Mercator projection and the drawing of the globe: 0° (Prime Meridian), 30°E, 30°W.

   How do the meridians on the Mercator projection differ from those on the

   drawing of the globe? _____

2. Trace these parallels in red on both the Mercator projection and the drawing of the globe: 0° (Equator), 30°N, 60°N.

   How do the parallels on the Mercator projection differ from those on the

   drawing of the globe? _____

3. An important advantage of the Mercator projection is that it does not distort directions. It is often used by sailors, who rely on accurate compass directions for navigation. Draw an arrow on the map from the first place to the second place. Write the direction of travel.

   a. London to Miami   _____

   b. New York City to Dakar   _____

Reading a Robinson Projection

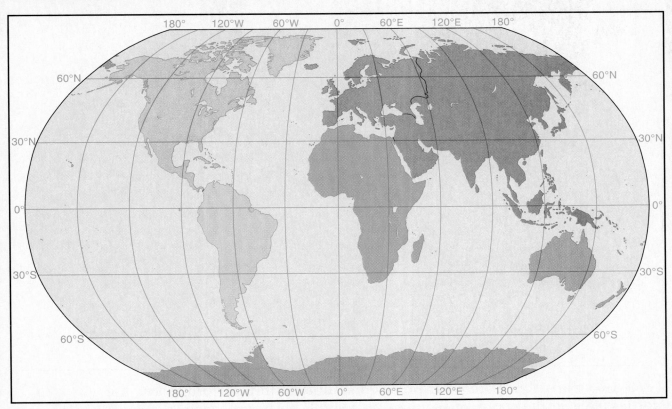

   Every flat map of Earth has distortion. The Robinson projection is no
different. It shows Antarctica as much larger than it actually is. Yet to many
people, the Robinson projection looks more like a globe than most other
projections. This is because the Robinson projection is a compromise of many
map distortions. You can think of a Robinson projection as having many
small distortions instead of a few large ones. The result is a map that looks
very much like a globe.

1. Label the seven continents on the Robinson projection above: North
   America, South America, Europe, Africa, Asia, Australia, and Antarctica.

2. Label these four oceans on the map: Arctic Ocean, Pacific Ocean, Atlantic
   Ocean, and Indian Ocean. (Label both areas of the Pacific Ocean.)

3. a. Are the parallels on the Robinson projection curved or straight? _____
   b. How do these compare with the parallels on a Mercator projection?

   _____

4. a. Are the meridians on a Robinson projection curved or straight? _____
   b. How do these compare with the meridians on a Mercator projection?

   _____

5. Draw a conclusion. Why do you think the Robinson projection shows a
   small part of Asia on the left-hand side of the map, when most of Asia

   is shown on the right-hand side? _____

Reading Polar Projections

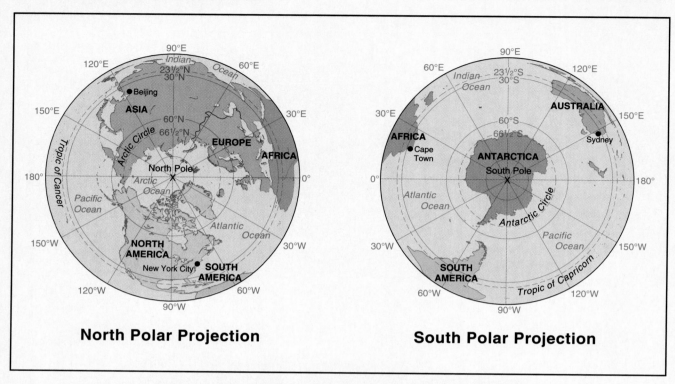

North Polar Projection　　　　**South Polar Projection**

The two maps above are polar projections. In a north polar projection, the North Pole is at the center of the map. In a south polar projection, the South Pole is at the center. Polar projections usually show one hemisphere. Like all flat maps of Earth, polar projections have distortion. Polar projections are more distorted toward the edges.

1. a. Which hemisphere is shown on a north polar projection? _____

   b. Which hemisphere is shown on a south polar projection? _____

2. Label the Equator on each of the two maps above.

3. Usually, north is at the top of a map. In a north polar projection, however, this isn't the case. Remember, the direction north is the direction toward the North Pole. In a north polar projection, the North Pole is in the center of the map. If you go from any point on the map toward the center, you are going north. Imagine you are traveling from the first place to the second place. Which direction will you travel?

   a. New York City to the North Pole　　　_____

   b. the North Pole to Beijing　　　_____

4. The direction south is the direction toward the South Pole. Study the south polar projection above. Imagine you are traveling from the first place to the second place. Which direction will you travel?

   a. Cape Town to the South Pole　　　_____

   b. the South Pole to Sydney　　　_____

Skill Check

Vocabulary Check   **Mercator projection**   **cartographers**
                                   Robinson projection   **polar projection**
                                   distortion   **projection**

Write the term that best completes each sentence.

1. People who make maps are known as _____ .

2. Because all projections of Earth show a curved surface on a flat map, they

    have _____ .

3. The _____ was created for sailors in the 1500s.

Map Check

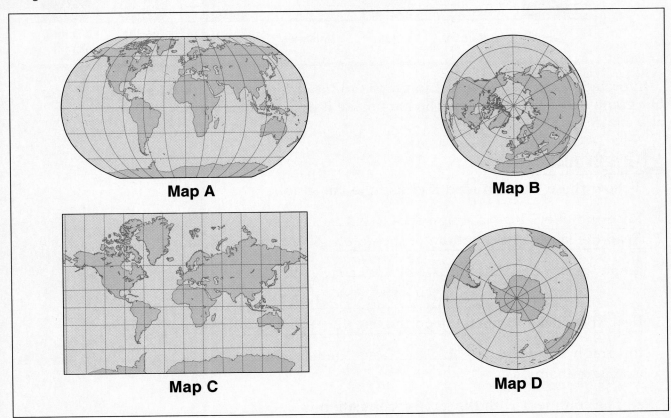

Map A

Map B

Map C

Map D

1. Identify each map projection.

   a. Map A is a _____ projection.

   b. Map B is a _____ projection.

   c. Map C is a _____ projection.

   d. Map D is a _____ projection.

2. Circle the projection that most closely resembles a globe.

12 • Graphs

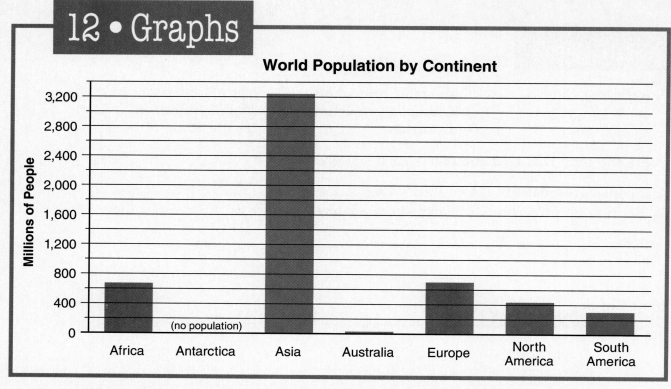

World Population by Continent

Information can be presented in graphs to make it easy to read. Bars on a **bar graph** stand for amounts. The bars make it easy to compare the amounts at a glance.

✔Graph Attack!

Follow these steps to read and use the bar graph.

1. <u>Read the title.</u> This bar graph shows _____.
2. <u>Read the labels at the bottom of the graph.</u> Name the areas shown on the

   graph. _____

   _____

3. <u>Read the label and numbers on the left side of the graph.</u> The numbers on

   the graph stand for _____.
4. <u>Compare the bars.</u>

   a. The continent with the largest population is _____.

   b. The continent with no population is _____.

   c. Estimate the population of North America. _____

   d. List the continents in order from greatest to least population. _____

   _____

5. <u>Draw a conclusion.</u> The population of Africa is about the same as the

   population of which other continent? _____

Reading a Bar Graph

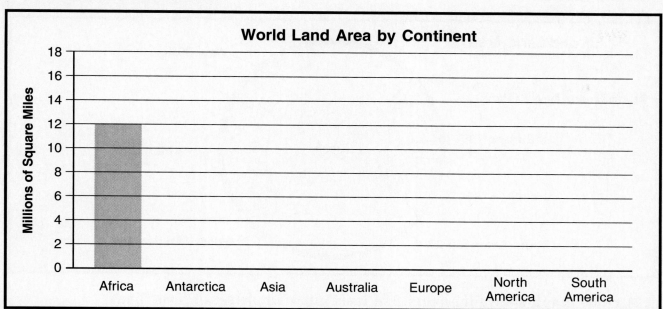

World Land Area by Continent

Millions of Square Miles

18
16
14
12
10
8
6
4
2
0

Africa   Antarctica   Asia   Australia   Europe   North America   South America

1. <u>Read the title.</u> This bar graph shows _____.
2. <u>Read the labels at the bottom of the graph.</u> Name the areas shown on the

   graph. _____

   _____
3. <u>Read the label and numbers on the left side of the graph.</u> The numbers on

   the graph stand for _____.
4. <u>Finish the graph.</u> Add bars to the graph to show the approximate area in square miles of the following continents:

Antarctica	5 million	Europe	4 million
Asia	17 million	North America	9 million
Australia	3 million	South America	7 million

5. <u>Compare the bars.</u>

   a. The largest continent is _____.

   b. The smallest continent is _____.

   c. Estimate the area of Africa. _____
6. <u>Draw a conclusion.</u>

   a. How do Africa and Europe compare in land area? _____

   b. Look back at the bar graph for population on page 70. How do Africa

   and Europe compare in population? _____

   c. Based on this information, do you think that Africa or Europe has more

   people per square mile? _____

Circle Graphs

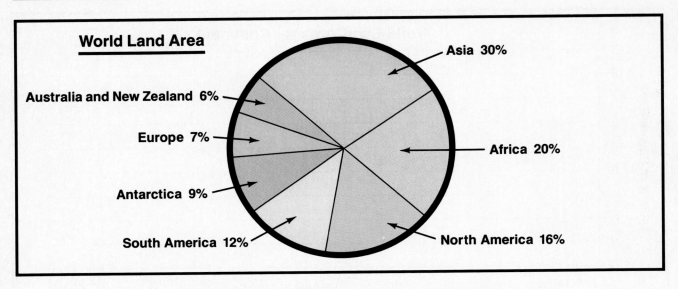

World Land Area

Asia 30%

Australia and New Zealand 6%

Europe 7%

Africa 20%

Antarctica 9%

South America 12%

North America 16%

A **circle graph** shows the parts that make up a whole set of facts. Each part of the graph is a percentage of the whole. All the parts together equal 100%. The circle graph on this page shows what percentage of all the land on Earth each continent includes.

✔ Graph Attack!

Follow these steps to read the circle graph.

1. Read the title. The whole circle stands for _____.
2. Read each part of the circle.

   a. Which continents are shown in this graph? _____

   _____.

   b. What percentage of Earth does each continent cover?

   North America _____   Europe _____   Asia _____

   South America _____   Africa _____   Antarctica _____

   c. Which continent covers the largest area of Earth's surface? _____

   d. Which continent covers the smallest area? _____
3. Compare the parts. Write <u>larger</u> or <u>smaller</u>.

   a. Asia is _____ than Africa.

   b. Europe is _____ than Australia and New Zealand.

   c. Australia and New Zealand are _____ than North America.
4. Draw a conclusion. Europe and Antarctica together are the same size as

   what continent? _____

Comparing Graphs

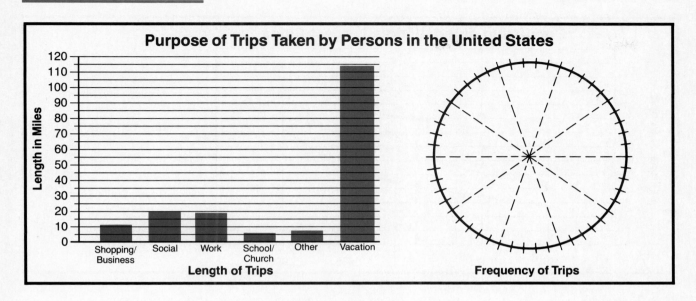

Purpose of Trips Taken by Persons in the United States

Length in Miles

Shopping/Business Social Work School/Church Other Vacation

Length of Trips

Frequency of Trips

1. Read the title.

   a. The bars on the bar graph and the parts of the circle graph stand

      for _____.

   b. The bar graph shows _____.

   c. The circle graph will show _____.

2. Finish the circle graph. Each dotted section represents 10% of the circle.
   Use the information below to finish the graph. Color and label each part.

Shopping/Business 34%	Social 27%	Work 22%
School/Church 12%	Other 4%	Vacation 1%

3. Read each graph.

   a. The longest trip is for _____.

   b. The shortest trip is for _____.

   c. Most trips are for _____.

   d. The fewest number of trips are for _____.

4. Compare the graphs.

   a. Which trip is the longest and taken least often? _____

   b. What is the length of the trip which is most often taken? _____

   c. Not including vacation, what two trips are longest?

      _____

   d. Out of 100 trips, how many of those long trips are taken? _____

Line Graphs

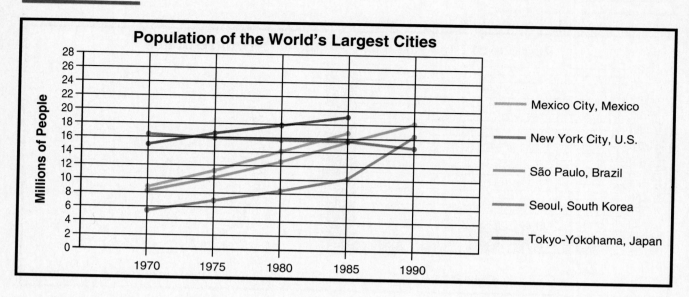

Population of the World's Largest Cities

Millions of People

1970 1975 1980 1985 1990

— Mexico City, Mexico
— New York City, U.S.
— São Paulo, Brazil
— Seoul, South Korea
— Tokyo-Yokohama, Japan

A **line graph** shows how amounts increase, decrease, or stay the same over periods of time.

☑Graph Attack!

Follow these steps to read and use the line graph.

1. Read the title. This line graph shows _____.

2. Read the numbers at the bottom of the graph. What do these numbers

   indicate? _____

3. Read the label and numbers on the left side of the graph. The numbers

   on the graph stand for _____.

4. Read the graph key. What does each line on the graph stand for?

   _____

5. Finish the graph. Use the information below to complete the graph.
   Population of Tokyo-Yokohama in 1990 = 27.0 million
   Population of Mexico City in 1990 = 20.2 million

6. Compare the lines.

   a. Which city had the largest population in 1970? _____

   b. Which city had the largest population in 1990? _____

   c. What year did São Paulo and New York City have about the same

      population? _____

7. Draw a conclusion. Each line on the graph goes generally up or generally down. These general directions are called trends. For example, the trend of the population of Mexico City is upwards. What is the trend of the

   population of New York City? _____

Combining Line and Bar Graphs

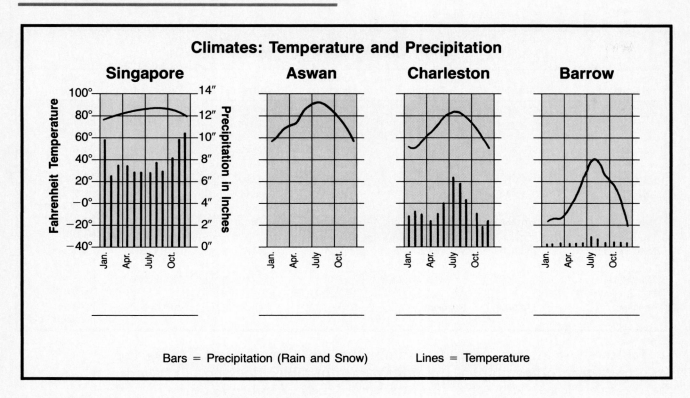

Climates: Temperature and Precipitation

Singapore   Aswan   Charleston   Barrow

Bars = Precipitation (Rain and Snow)   Lines = Temperature

1. Read the title. The graphs show _____.
2. Read the numbers along the sides of the graph. The numbers on the

   left sides indicate _____.

   The numbers on the right sides indicate _____.

3. Read the words along the bottom. The words indicate _____.
4. Compare the graphs.
   a. Which place has the greatest amount of precipitation?

   _____

   b. Which place has the lowest temperature? _____
   c. Which place has the least change in temperature over the year?

   _____

   d. Which place has the greatest change in precipitation over the year?

   _____

5. Draw a conclusion. Label each place with the climate zone that best
   fits it.

   Temperate = warm and rainy summer, mild and rainy winter
   Desert = hot and dry all year
   Tropical = hot and rainy all year
   Polar = cold and dry all year

Tables

Eight Countries of the World						
Country	Area	Capital	Official Language	Unit of Currency	Population	Highest Point
Brazil	8,511,965	Brasília	Portuguese	Cruzeiro	133,882,000	2890 m Pico da Bandeira
Canada	9,976,139	Ottawa	French English	Dollar	24,620,000	6050 m Mt. Logan
Denmark	43,069	Copenhagen	Danish	Krone	5,175,000	173 m
Egypt	1,001,449	Cairo	Arabic	Pound	43,611,000	2637 m Jabal Katrinah
Italy	301,268	Rome	Italian	Lira	57,838,000	4731 m Mt. Blanc
New Zealand	268,676	Wellington	English	Dollar	3,400,000	3764 m Mt. Cook
Tanzania	945,087	Dar es Salaam	English Swahili	Shilling	19,388,000	5895 m Kilimanjaro
Thailand	514,000	Bangkok	Thai	Baht	49,414,000	2595 m Inthanon Peak

Tables show a large amount of information in a small space. Unlike the information in other graphs, the information in tables does not all have to be the same kind. This table shows several kinds of information.

☑ Table Attack!

Follow these steps to read a table.

1. Read the title. This table shows _____ .
2. Read the words along the top and the left side of the table.

   a. What countries are shown in this table? _____

   _____

   b. Name four pieces of information you can learn. _____

   _____

3. Read the table.

   a. What is the largest country in area? _____

   b. What is the least populated country listed? _____

   c. What and where is the highest point listed? _____

4. Draw a conclusion.

   a. Which are the two largest countries in area? _____ _____

   b. Which of those has the smaller population? _____

   c. Which has the greater population density? _____

Comparing a Table and a Map

Flights from Chicago				Time Zones in North America

Departure Time	Arrival Time	Airline Flight #	Meal
To Acapulco			
8:55 AM	1:21 PM	AA 169	B
9:30 AM	3:15 PM	MX 803	LS
To Bermuda			
8:05 AM	3:40 PM	DL 88	BL
To Calgary			
10:00 AM	2:30 PM	UA 933	L
10:30 AM	3:00 PM	AC 833	L
To Mexico City			
1:50 AM	5:30 AM	MX 181	D
9:30 AM	1:10 PM	MX 803	L
3:45 PM	10:35 PM	MX 815	LS
9:50 PM	1:57 AM	AA 57	S
To Milwaukee			
7:00 AM	7:50 AM	AA 1241	
9:55 AM	10:31 AM	UA 559	
6:34 PM	7:16 PM	AA 205	
To Montreal			
7:10 AM	10:10 AM	AA 696	B
1:12 PM	4:12 PM	AA 286	S
5:40 PM	8:40 PM	AA 410	D

B - Breakfast   D - Dinner   DL - Delta Airlines
L - Lunch   AA - American Airlines   MX - Mexicana Airlines
S - Snack   AC - Air Canada   UA - United Airlines

1. Read the title.

   a. This table shows _____.

   b. The map shows _____.

2. Read the words along the top and the left side of the table.

   a. The flights from Chicago are to _____
   _____.

   b. What are two pieces of information you can learn about these
   flights? _____

3. Read the table key. What do the letters AA stand for? _____

   L? _____ MX? _____ S? _____

4. Compare the chart and the map.
   a. To which cities could you fly from Chicago without changing time
   zones?_____

   b. How many time zones do you cross to fly from Chicago to Calgary? __

   c. If you left Chicago at 10:00 AM, what time would you arrive in
   Calgary? _____

   d. When you arrive in Calgary, what time is it in Chicago? _____

   e. How long was your trip? _____

   f. How long is the trip from Chicago to Montreal? _____

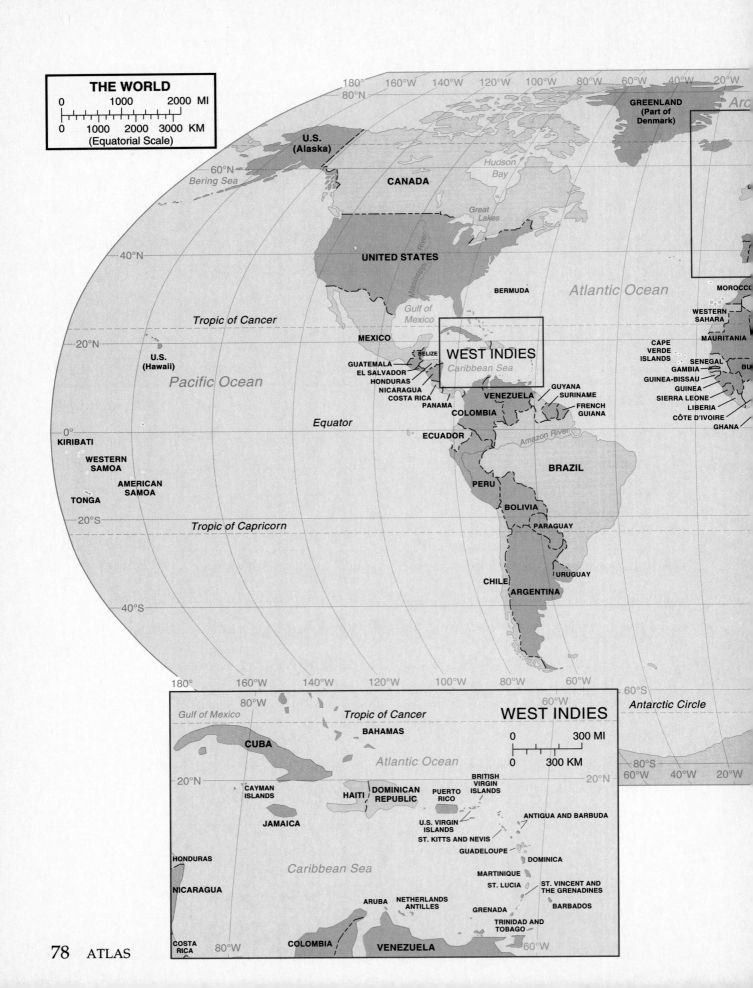

THE WORLD

0   1000   2000 MI

0   1000   2000   3000 KM
(Equatorial Scale)

180°   160°W   140°W   120°W   100°W   80°W   60°W   40°W   20°W

80°N

Arc

GREENLAND
(Part of
Denmark)

60°N

Bering Sea

U.S.
(Alaska)

CANADA

*Hudson
Bay*

*Great
Lakes*

40°N

UNITED STATES

Mississippi River

BERMUDA

Atlantic Ocean

MOROCCO

WESTERN
SAHARA

Tropic of Cancer

*Gulf of
Mexico*

MAURITANIA

20°N

MEXICO

BELIZE

WEST INDIES

CAPE
VERDE
ISLANDS

SENEGAL

U.S.
(Hawaii)

Pacific Ocean

GUATEMALA
EL SALVADOR
HONDURAS
NICARAGUA
COSTA RICA
PANAMA

Caribbean Sea

GUYANA
SURINAME

FRENCH
GUIANA

GAMBIA
GUINEA-BISSAU
GUINEA
SIERRA LEONE
LIBERIA
CÔTE D'IVOIRE
GHANA

VENEZUELA

COLOMBIA

Equator

ECUADOR

Amazon River

BRAZIL

0°

KIRIBATI

WESTERN
SAMOA

AMERICAN
SAMOA

PERU

TONGA

BOLIVIA

20°S

Tropic of Capricorn

PARAGUAY

URUGUAY

CHILE

ARGENTINA

40°S

180°   160°W   140°W   120°W   100°W   80°W   60°W

60°S

Antarctic Circle

80°W

80°S

60°W   40°W   20°W

Gulf of Mexico

Tropic of Cancer

60°W

WEST INDIES

0   300 MI

0   300 KM

CUBA

BAHAMAS

Atlantic Ocean

20°N

CAYMAN
ISLANDS

HAITI

DOMINICAN
REPUBLIC

PUERTO
RICO

BRITISH
VIRGIN
ISLANDS

20°N

JAMAICA

U.S. VIRGIN
ISLANDS

ST. KITTS AND NEVIS

ANTIGUA AND BARBUDA

GUADELOUPE

DOMINICA

HONDURAS

Caribbean Sea

MARTINIQUE

ST. LUCIA

ST. VINCENT AND
THE GRENADINES

NICARAGUA

ARUBA

NETHERLANDS
ANTILLES

GRENADA

BARBADOS

TRINIDAD AND
TOBAGO

COSTA
RICA

80°W

COLOMBIA

VENEZUELA

60°W

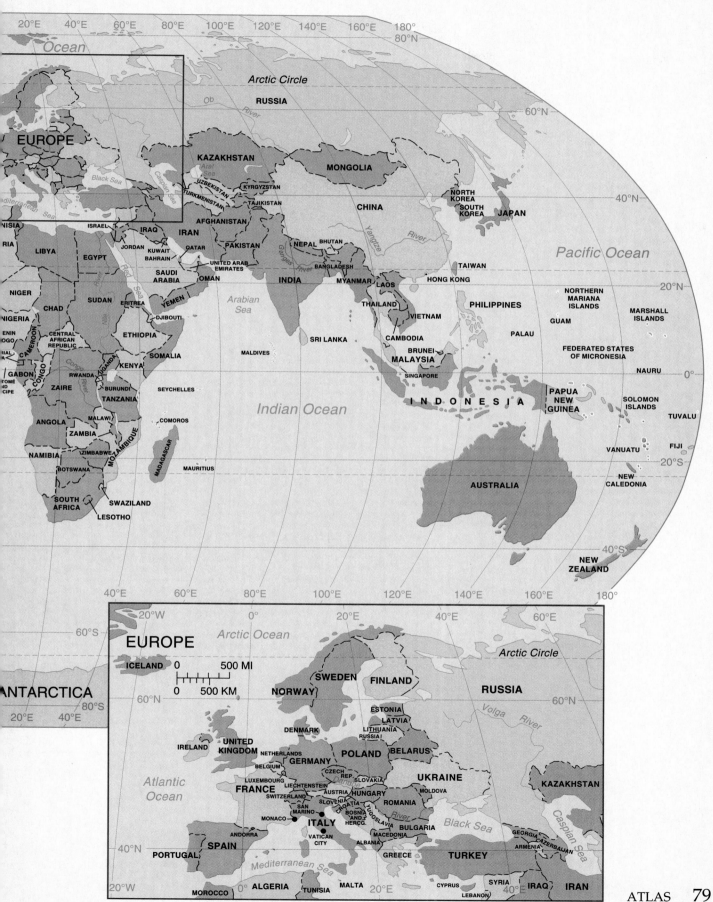

Ocean

Arctic Circle

20°E 40°E 60°E 80°E 100°E 120°E 140°E 160°E 180° 80°N

RUSSIA 60°N

Ob River

EUROPE

Black Sea

KAZAKHSTAN

Aral Sea

Caspian Sea

UZBEKISTAN KYRGYZSTAN

MONGOLIA

TURKMENISTAN

TAJIKISTAN 40°N

NORTH KOREA

SOUTH KOREA JAPAN

NISIA

RIA

ISRAEL IRAQ IRAN AFGHANISTAN

Mediterranean Sea

JORDAN KUWAIT QATAR BAHRAIN

PAKISTAN CHINA

NEPAL BHUTAN

Yangtze River

River

Pacific Ocean

LIBYA EGYPT

UNITED ARAB EMIRATES

Ganges River

BANGLADESH 20°N

TAIWAN

Red Sea

SAUDI ARABIA

OMAN

INDIA

MYANMAR

LAOS

HONG KONG

NIGER CHAD SUDAN ERITREA YEMEN

Nile

Arabian Sea

THAILAND

VIETNAM

PHILIPPINES

NORTHERN MARIANA ISLANDS

MARSHALL ISLANDS

NIGERIA DJIBOUTI

CAMBODIA

GUAM

ENIN OGO CENTRAL AFRICAN REPUBLIC ETHIOPIA

SRI LANKA

MALDIVES

BRUNEI MALAYSIA

PALAU

FEDERATED STATES OF MICRONESIA

IAL CAMEROON

SOMALIA

SINGAPORE

NAURU 0°

TOMÉ ND CIPE GABON CONGO RWANDA UGANDA KENYA

Congo River

ZAIRE BURUNDI

TANZANIA

SEYCHELLES

INDONESIA

PAPUA NEW GUINEA

SOLOMON ISLANDS

TUVALU

ANGOLA MALAWI

Indian Ocean

COMOROS

ZAMBIA

NAMIBIA ZIMBABWE MOZAMBIQUE

MADAGASCAR

MAURITIUS

VANUATU

FIJI

NEW CALEDONIA 20°S

BOTSWANA

AUSTRALIA

SOUTH AFRICA SWAZILAND

LESOTHO

40°S

NEW ZEALAND

40°E 60°E 80°E 100°E 120°E 140°E 160°E 180°

60°S

ANTARCTICA 80°S

20°E 40°E

EUROPE

20°W 0° 20°E 40°E 60°E

Arctic Ocean

Arctic Circle

ICELAND

0 500 MI

0 500 KM

SWEDEN FINLAND

RUSSIA

NORWAY

Volga River

60°N

60°N

ESTONIA

LATVIA

DENMARK

LITHUANIA

RUSSIA

IRELAND UNITED KINGDOM

NETHERLANDS

GERMANY

POLAND

BELARUS

BELGIUM

CZECH REP.

Danube

UKRAINE

KAZAKHSTAN

Atlantic Ocean

LUXEMBOURG

LIECHTENSTEIN

SLOVAKIA

FRANCE

SWITZERLAND

AUSTRIA HUNGARY

MOLDOVA

SLOVENIA CROATIA

ROMANIA

SAN MARINO

BOSNIA AND HERCG.

YUGOSLAVIA

River

Black Sea

Caspian Sea

MONACO

ITALY

BULGARIA

GEORGIA AZERBAIJAN

ANDORRA

VATICAN CITY

MACEDONIA

ARMENIA

40°N SPAIN

ALBANIA

PORTUGAL

Mediterranean Sea

GREECE

TURKEY

20°W 0° ALGERIA TUNISIA MALTA 20°E

CYPRUS SYRIA IRAQ IRAN

MOROCCO LEBANON 40°E

THE UNITED STATES

| International Boundary |
| State Boundary |
| ✪ National Capital |
| ★ State Capital |

0 100 200 300 400 500 MI
0 100 200 300 400 500 600 700 800 KM

Pacific Ocean

Hawaii
Honolulu ★
0 50 100 MI
0 50 100 KM

Alaska
RUSSIA
CANADA
Juneau ★
Yukon River
Arctic Ocean
0 200 400 MI
0 200 400 KM

MEXICO

California
Sacramento ★
Sierra Nevada
Nevada
Carson City ★
Oregon
Salem ★
Washington
Olympia ★
Columbia River
Cascade Range

Arizona
Phoenix ★
Colorado River
Utah
Salt Lake City ★
Great Salt Lake
Idaho
Boise ★
Helena ★
Snake River
Montana
Rocky Mountains
Wyoming
Cheyenne ★

New Mexico
Santa Fe ★
Colorado
Denver ★
Rio Grande

Texas
Austin ★
Brazos River
Oklahoma
Oklahoma City ★
Red River
Kansas
Topeka ★
Arkansas River
Nebraska
Lincoln ★
South Dakota
Pierre ★
North Dakota
Bismarck ★
Minnesota
St. Paul ★
Red River
Missouri River

Louisiana
Baton Rouge ★
Arkansas
Little Rock ★
Mississippi River
Missouri
Jefferson City ★
Iowa
Des Moines ★
Wisconsin
Madison ★
Lake Superior

Mississippi
Jackson ★
Alabama
Montgomery ★
Tennessee
Nashville ★
Kentucky
Frankfort ★
Illinois
Springfield ★
Indiana
Indianapolis ★
Ohio River
Lake Michigan
Michigan
Lansing ★
Lake Huron

Georgia
Atlanta ★
Florida
Tallahassee ★
Lake Okeechobee
South Carolina
Columbia ★
North Carolina
Raleigh ★
Appalachian Mountains
West Virginia
Charleston ★
Virginia
Richmond ★
Ohio
Columbus ★
Lake Erie
Lake Ontario
CANADA

Gulf of Mexico
Atlantic Ocean

Pennsylvania
Harrisburg ★
New York
Albany ★
Washington, D.C. ✪
Maryland
Annapolis ★
Delaware
Dover ★
New Jersey
Trenton ★
Connecticut
Hartford ★
Rhode Island
Providence ★
Massachusetts
Boston ★
New Hampshire
Concord ★
Vermont
Montpelier ★
Maine
Augusta ★

N

80 ATLAS